The Other Me

My Journey with Tourette's Syndrome

Esmail "Johnny" Bahar

Dear Reader:

Welcome to the journey of my life with Tourette's syndrome. This book is about what I've gone through and what I will continue to face for the rest of my life. I hope you will come to understand Tourette's and will gain a different outlook on individuals who are dealing with this challenging syndrome. This book contains some "R" and "X"-rated material. Please do not be offended by the curses and disturbing statements about race, gender, and ethnicity. I want you to know that I am opposed to all forms of prejudice and discrimination, but my Tourette's is not. I wish I could be "normal," but the *other me* is in control.

Thank you and God Bless.

Esmail Bahar

D1635944

ISBN: 978-1-4276-2131-3

Published by:
Esmail "Johnny" Bahar
P.O. Box 1088
French Camp, CA 95231

I dedicate this book to

my beautiful wife

Weda Shah.

Acknowledgments

I would like to thank my wife, Weda Shah, for encouraging me to write the story of my life and for being my strongest support in life, after God.

I would also like to thank my loving family for being there for me from the beginning, and also thank my wife's loving family for supporting and understanding my journey with Tourette's. Thanks also to the people around me who have believed in me for being funny and strong. Finally, I'd like to thank my editor for his help in presenting my story.

Table of Contents

Chapter 1
Before the War

My name is Esmail. All my friends call me Johnny, so you can call me Johnny too. I have Tourette's syndrome.

What is Tourette's?

Do you really want to know what it is? Well, I'll tell you: it's a syndrome that causes involuntary tics, twitches and swearing.

This book is about my struggle and journey with Tourette's, and how it has been both my nemesis and my good friend. Some people might think I'm a psychopath when they see me in public, but in fact I'm a family man with a beautiful wife and three wonderful kids as well as a successful account executive for a mortgage company. Just because I say and do offensive things on a daily basis doesn't mean I'm a bad guy. I don't intend to curse or hurt anyone. My Tourette's syndrome makes me say things I don't want to say, and do things I don't want to do, but I can't help it.

For instance, once I went to Starbucks to get a coffee. When it was my turn to order, I asked the girl to give me an "extra large Mocha black dick." She looked at me in astonishment and said, "Excuse me."

1

Trying to cover up what my Tourette's had said, I replied, "Excuse me, what did you hear?"

"Did you say something nasty?" she asked. "I thought I heard something nasty."

"I didn't," I insisted.

She seemed almost convinced and then said, "Okay, so you want a Mocha, right?"

Then my Tourette's replied, "Yes, with some sperm cream."

She freaked out and said in a harsh voice, "We don't have a big Mocha black dick here, and we don't have sperm cream!" Then she looked over at the manager, who had overheard our conversation. The two of them told me to leave or they would call the cops.

I feel ashamed for having Tourette's, but who am I to control it? And why should I feel ashamed? I am trying my best, but my syndrome has a mind of its own. Tourette's has more control than I have.

During my nearly three decades of living with Tourette's, I have experienced the most terrible and embarrassing moments as well as the most exciting and happy ones. As a child and teenager, I was so depressed that I attempted suicide many times but somehow miraculously survived. When I turned nineteen and survived another attempt, I began to think that God wanted me to live. If he didn't, I wouldn't be here telling you this story. From that time on, I did everything I could to become strong and survive the syndrome. And I've done it. I'm strong, positive, and help a lot of friends, family members and relatives with their challenges, financial and otherwise. Some live here in America, and the rest live in Afghanistan. I also have a strong and wonderful wife who helped make me who I am today.

Let me give you one more example of Tourette's before I tell you the story of my life, from childhood to manhood. One day I went to 7eleven to get coffee and saw a blond lady buying a hot dog with her teenage daughter and son. I was waiting in line behind her and watching her eat the hot dog. The Tourette's suddenly said, "Suck it baby! Eat it hard! Suck it baby! Eat it hard! Take the juice out!"

"What did you say?" the lady asked.

"Dick, dick, dick, big cow dick," My Tourette's said.

"Excuse me!"

Then her daughter chimed in, "This dirty Mexican is nasty."

"No, no, no. I have Tourette's," I said.

"So fucking what," the mother said. "I have a Honda Accord outside. So what if you have a fucking Taurus, dumbass!"

"I didn't say 'Taurus' – I said 'Tourette's'."

"Fuck your car! Fuck you!" she shouted. "What the fuck are you saying? If my husband were here, he'd make you suck this hotdog."

She never gave me a chance to explain. She just started cursing me, and so did her daughter and son. When they left and got into their car, the mother flipped me the bird as they were pulling away.

When it came my turn to pay the 7eleven clerk, who was wearing a turban, he said, "Don't say that shit again in my store about hot dog because I lose customers."

"I have fucking Tourette's," I said.

"I'm not a fucking terrorist," he screeched. "You goddammed Mexican, get out of my store!"

He took my coffee and said, "Get the fuck out!" He too didn't give me a chance to explain.

You'll be hearing even more bizarre but true stories about my life with Tourette's. I'll begin my story by telling you what my life was like before my syndrome surfaced.

I was born in Kabul on January 5, 1972. Kabul is the capital of Afghanistan, a largely Muslim country bordered by Pakistan to the east and south, by Iran to the west, and by the former Soviet Union to the north.

I am the third son in a family of six children. I have two older brothers, a younger brother and two younger sisters. All of us except my youngest brother were born in Kabul. All but him grew up spoiled brats!

Living in Kabul, we were surrounded by nothing but beauty. Kabul is a cosmopolitan city that blends the new and the old, the modern and the ancient. It is an urban center as lovely and crowded as downtown San Francisco. When I was a kid, its great restaurants and hotels used to attract thousands of tourists from Europe and America.

What made Kabul most exciting in those days was its street life. There you could find grocers selling fresh fruits and vegetables on their stands, shoemakers fashioning sandals and shoes from lambskin, and old men sitting on the ground with their hookah pipes, smoking hashish and drinking tea from beautiful ceramic cups. Some men would be chewing naswar, a green tobacco, or holding it under their tongues. Nearby was a toofdani, a metal spittoon shaped like an hour glass. Elderly ladies would be purchasing big sacks of rice, flour, tomatoes and potatoes, and sometimes would hire porters to pull the groceries in their Karachi wagons, with the long wooden handles on their shoulders. There were also porters carrying on their shoulders big jugs of water. Occasionally, you might even see a bird fight, with men betting on different bodana birds.

Outside restaurants you sometimes saw midget waiters with big black moustaches and white turbans, drumming up business for their proprietors. "Come in, come in," they would say. "We have fresh kabob today. Come join us, we have empty space for the lovers, even private rooms for the ladies." Some of the midgets wore hats with signs that said, "May the evil eye stay away!" There were also men who walked around with metal buckets filled with hot coals. These spandis sold you seeds, which you tossed into the fire. The smoke from the burning seeds purified you and protected you from the evil eye.

On many street corners you could see little ladies sitting and selling bangles. Sometimes, a group of school girls, outfitted in black dresses and white scarves, would be standing around them, trying bangles on their thin wrists. At other corners you saw nan wai, the men who baked fresh breads in clay ovens. You could buy the dough from them, or if you couldn't afford it, you could bring your own, and they would bake it for you. As the breads baked, families would chat and play and laugh. When it was winter time, the children used their bread baskets for sleds and dusted them off when the bread was finished. Sometimes the boys brought their colorful kites to compete. The object was to fly your kite the highest and be the last kite flying.

The kids might even play marbles or engage in egg battles. Each child had boiled and colored an egg. They would knock the hard-boiled eggs together to determine who was strongest.

As a child, I participated in many of these egg battles. One time especially stands out in my memory. It was just before the big feast of Eid that takes place after Ramadan, the month when Muslims fast all day and eat only at night. The feast of Eid is held for three days. Everybody was looking forward to it and was going shopping for new clothes, gifts and sweets. During these three days, people visit relatives, go places, attend festivals, and play games such as bird fighting, marbles, and egg battles.

The day before the Eid began I went to the store and purchased twenty big white eggs. I told the store owner that if he gave me good eggs and I won the game, I would bring him back some souvenir. So he gave me some really nice eggs and wished me good luck. I still remember his old wrinkled face with a white beard and a big mole on the corner of his lip. He wore traditional Afghani clothes: the all-white paran and the tonban as well as the white turban with black stripes.

I brought the eggs home and got ready for the egg battle. Then I called my cousins and brothers to tell them I was going to play egg fighting the next day and would bet 50 Afghani rupees (equal to $100 now) against anyone who was willing to compete against me. They all took up my challenge and agreed to meet me the next day.

That night I boiled the eggs myself, without my mom's permission, and let them cook for almost 25 minutes. Then I painted all of the eggs pink. In the middle of each egg, I painted yellow stripes, and in the stripes I drew stars with a moon. I wanted my eggs to look very beautiful! When the paint dried, I put all the eggs under my parents' bed, so no one would touch or break them. But all night long I was worried about whether my eggs were safe. Maybe they had been broken or stolen by my brothers.

In the morning I went to my mom and dad's room to get the eggs and saw dad looking at them with a big smile on his face. Suddenly, I got really worried that he was going to throw them away, so I started to scream to call everyone and tell them what dad was about to do. But then I remembered that it was the Eid, and during the feast, no one can say or do anything bad to anybody because it is a day of love and affection. So I ran to my dad and asked him, "Dad, do you like my drawing?"

"Yes, I love it," he replied. "It is just like my drawing when I was almost your age and drew my first eggs with the same design. Good job!"

He handed me the eggs and wished me good luck. I ran to the first floor to show my eggs to my grandfather, but he had gone hours earlier to the mosque to say Eid prayers. My grandmother told me he would be back in a couple of hours, and then we would all celebrate the Eid festival. Traditionally, during the morning time, all of the men go to the mosque for the Eid prayer. After the prayer, everybody hugs and kisses each other at the mosque and then come home to their families to start the festival. Adults give gifts of money to their children. These gifts are known as Eidi. It is very important for children to receive Eidi, and they look forward to these gifts during the previous year. If you don't give a child Eidi, it is almost insulting and hurtful.

So I waited and waited for grandfather and the rest of the men from the household to come back from the mosque to start the Eid celebration. Time was passing by very slowly, and I was losing my patience minute by minute. Then suddenly I heard my brothers calling out, "It is Eid. It is Eid. It is Eid." I ran and gave grandfather a big hug and kissed his hands. It is a tradition to kiss an elder's hand. I told him, "Happy Eid, grandfather!" He kissed me back and gave me my Eidi. It was 200 Afghani rupees! That made me the happiest boy on the block.

Now it was time for the egg battle. I ran to my brothers and cousins (all older than I) and told them to start the egg fighting. They weren't ready because they had attended the mosque ceremony with the rest of the men in the house. So I had to wait for them. Meanwhile, I went to my dad and said "Happy Eid." I also greeted the rest of the family and collected my Eidi from almost all of them.

Finally, my brother and cousins were ready for the egg battle. My brother Akbar said to me, "You're going to lose all your Eidi to me because you're not going to win this game from me."

I laughed at him and said, "My eggs are the best!" Then I turned to the others and said, "Don't count on winning!"

The first person I played was Akbar. He pulled his eggs out: they were very ugly and colorless. I shouted at him, "Didn't you have time to at least color you're eggs?! Oh, oh, how ugly and terrible they look!"

"Let's go for the win," I said as I pulled out my eggs.

Akbar was surprised how nice and beautiful they were. He said, "Oh, oh, the little Esmail was busy. You must have been awake all night coloring your eggs."

His comment made me very happy and proud. I said, "Are you sure you want to play with me?"

"Yes, little boy, let's go," he replied, "and don't brag about it any more."

So we started the game. Almost every family member came to watch us. I was concentrating very hard and was showing off my work to everyone. Akbar started laughing and said, "Little boy, put your money on the floor so we can start."

I pulled 50 rupees from my pocket and put them on the floor. I also told Akbar to put his money on the floor since I didn't trust him. In fact, I asked my grandfather to come and be the middle man. He gladly accepted the invitation and joined us.

The game started. We stood about three feet apart. Each of us held out an egg in our right hand and alternated tapping the other's egg. Soon Akbar's egg got a crack on it. After a few more poundings, his egg was smashed, and I became the winner. It was my first egg battle and first win! Grandfather was very proud of me and said that tomorrow he would take me to the big egg fighting festival where hundreds of people gathered to fight eggs. The news really excited me!

The next day we entered the big crowded park, where there were lots of trees and a man-made pond, as well as many vendors selling ice cream, cookies, bread, cream rolls and other goodies. Hundreds of men were sitting on the ground with their colorful eggs decorated with beautiful designs. There were also police guards patrolling the grounds. The sight of all those people overwhelmed me, and I almost lost my confidence because I knew that many of those men were professional game players. I worried that my eggs were not good enough to fight the eggs of the professionals. I almost chickened out, but my grandfather told me that my eggs were the best and that I was going to be the winner. Because I cared about him and didn't want him to think I was a coward, I couldn't tell him how I felt.

Grandfather walked up to a group of men sitting on their carpets and said, "Whoever plays with my grandson and wins, I will give that person 100 Afghani rupees." A large crowd of men got up from their carpets and headed toward us, and I heard them saying, "I'll play the boy. Bring him here."

Feeling very nervous, I said, "Grandfather, let's go home and not play."

He said, "Son, don't be scared. You're the best, and you're my grandson."

From all the men who approached us, grandfather chose only five people. The first guy I had to play was about 15 years old. His eggs were nicely colored green and lavender. In less than ten seconds, he broke my eggs! I was really mad and wanted to cry, but grandfather comforted me and said, "It's okay."

Then I played the second guy. He had beautiful red and yellow eggs. In a few seconds, I broke his eggs, and he was out of the game!

"Wow, I won, I won!" I told my grandfather as I jumped up and down with happiness.

The third guy had only yellow eggs. I beat him too!

The fourth guy was a 13 year-old-boy with boogers in his nose. He looked very dirty as if he had just fixed a car. But he had really nice, multicolored eggs. Smiling at me, he said, "Let's play my man."

Within a few seconds, he cracked my eggs a little bit. I became nervous that I was losing the game. But as we continued, I cracked his egg in two places. And in a few more seconds, I succeeded in breaking his egg entirely, so he was out of the game.

The last guy I played was a 35-year-old man with a long black beard. He wore a hat on his head and a big brown shawl with green stripes over his shoulder. He was a very weird man and pulled out some eggs that were very different from all of the other eggs we had seen. His eggs were much bigger and thicker and were painted with several colors. The bottoms of the eggs had some sort of golden color which I had never seen before.

I asked the man, "Did you do this egg yourself?"

He didn't reply but said, "Let's play the game, young boy."

We played for almost a minute, and neither of our eggs cracked. Suddenly, my egg started to show signs of a crack. I was shaking and did not want to lose this game. In a few more seconds I was out of the game. He had won the last game!

My grandfather looked at me and said, "Don't worry. You have won three out of five games, so you're the winner!"

It was a very beautiful experience to be inside the crowd and to actually play the game with professionals.

Kabul is a city of rich and poor. I had the good fortune of growing up in a wealthy and well known family. My mother's father was a successful and respected businessman, and my father's father was a decorated General in the Afghani army. Both men were renowned in the community, and even today, their names are known by many Kabulese.

My immediate family lived mainly with my mother's parents. My grandfather owned a beautiful brick mansion located about ten minutes by foot from downtown Kabul. We also spent some time with my father's parents, who lived across the street about a half block away.

My grandfather's mansion was as grand as a castle. It had three stories with dozens of rooms on each floor as well as a huge yard, longer than a football field! Guards were on duty at the gate and around the house. On the first floor were the guest rooms for relatives and friends. On the second floor was a kickback place: a big living room with a TV as well as the bedrooms of my grandparents and family. The third floor was a kind of play room with a balcony. On all four sides were windows, so we could see the stores, cars, school, theatre and neighborhood streets. From the roof of the house you could see the beautiful mountains located just outside the city limits. On some of those mountains were stone houses. It was almost like being in Lake Tahoe. Yes, we had it good!

Around the time I was born, my grandfather became wealthy from manufacturing clothes, mainly shirts. Later, he went into the construction business. Because he was well off, lots of people would have loved to kidnap him or us kids and ask for a ransom of millions of dollars. In those days, kidnappers thought nothing of killing their captives if the ransom wasn't paid!

But my brothers and I weren't afraid. Life was easy back then. We felt protected by the guards and also had four servants. One lady cooked and served our food. Another lady baked all the cookies and sweets. A man baked the breads on a big stove, and a driver took us wherever we wanted to go. There were different cooking shifts day and night. Food was ready before we woke up!

Grandfather was a very generous man. On Fridays at the mosque and also on Sunday mornings, he gave away hundreds of loaves of breads to the poor – as well as other kinds of food and lots of money. I loved him to death – he was a great man – and I learned a lot from his heart. If you came up to him and asked for money, he would give it to you without even asking why you needed it. He wouldn't even ask you when you planned to pay him back. You knew he trusted you with everything he had. If you didn't pay him back, he wouldn't press charges. He always said, "I leave it all up to God (Allah). God decides what we did wrong when we go up there."

I never knew my grandfather to do anything wrong. He always served the poor and prayed everyday. My family only says good things about him. Because he was such a great man, my brothers and I called him our "great grandfather." I believe that if he were alive today, he would be president of Afghanistan since he was so well known and well loved by everyone. My brothers and I called him "the Elvis guy" because of his reknown.

Grandfather took care of us kids with his heart. I remember that every New Year's time, we would get into his big car, and he would drive us around the city with lots of money in his pockets and with wrapped gifts that filled the car. We helped him distribute the money and gifts to the poor. Behind us were another three or four cars doing the same thing: passing out grandfather's presents.

When I was growing up, grandfather looked very young, though I am sure he was in his mid-50s. He was a handsome, well-dressed man who always wore a suit and tie – even inside the house! He wore fine suits, like the kind the Italian Mafioso wear! To me he looked like a sheik, a king, especially when he sat in his beautiful chair, made of hand-carved wood, burgundy leather, and gold-colored trim. At bedtime, he wore a man's silk gown, either burgundy or gray, that had matching slippers.

Grandfather named me and my brothers. When I was born, he was on one of the few business trips he ever took. He called in, and my parents told him they had named me "Mustafa." He said, "I want you to call him Esmail." So that became my name. Esmail (Ishmael) was the first born son of the prophet Ibrahim (Abraham), who is the forefather of both the Hebrew and Arabic peoples. My last name, "Bahar," means "Spring."

My grandmother was very different than my grandfather. We called her "the Airplane" because she was always going on trips alone around the world, especially to Europe. Grandfather almost never traveled. He preferred staying at home (and in that way I am now a lot like him). Grandmother enjoyed looking good and wore expensive clothes and jewelry. She was nice, but my brothers and I weren't as close to her.

My father's father was a tough, bald, army General. He also owned a huge mansion as well as a hundred-room apartment building. He was famous for catching the most wanted fugitives in the country. Though he got shot and stabbed, he managed to bring the fugitives to justice. Unfortunately, even at home he treated everyone like they were in the military! If you tried to speak up, he would say, "Shut the hell up! Shut the hell up!" He was definitely the guy in charge, the man who gave the orders. You just had to listen and obey. He didn't have a heart like my mother's father, but I guess he needed to be tough to succeed in the army.

I hate to admit it, but my father's father used to beat my mom. I can remember bruises on her back and even on her face. The beatings would usually happen while my dad was away on business. Dad was originally in business with his father but then started his own trucking business. Often he would be away for months at a time transporting cars and food supplies back and forth between Afghanistan and Germany. So my grandfather, and even my grandmother, could treat my mother any way they wanted. When dad returned from his trip, mom would cover up the beating and say she had fallen. Sometimes dad would find out what really happened, and then he'd get mad. But there wasn't much he could do. As long as he was living in his father's house, he had to respect his father. His father was in charge.

My grandfather didn't only beat my mother. He also beat the wives of his other sons. He demanded total obedience. With his wife, he had over 30 children, though only about a dozen are alive today (some of them died from childhood illnesses). It was easy to raise a lot of kids because my grandparents had so many servants working for them.

You might wonder why my family didn't move out of my father's parents' house altogether. In Afghani culture, newlyweds move in with the man's parents. If you move out, it is seen as looking for a divorce, and we don't believe in divorce. If my parents moved out, the whole community would have found out, and it would have brought a bad reputation to the family. I can say now that the part of our tradition that allows the beating of women is simply wrong.

Our family used to move back and forth between the two mansions. At both places we had our own rooms, which really amounted to our own house. The mansions were like castles with dozens of furnished rooms on each floor. Life was happy when we stayed with mom's parents, and sad when we stayed with dad's parents. Two sides of my life on two sides of the same street! We might stay a week at one house and a week at the other, or a month at one and a month at the other. Back and forth, back and forth. We lived in both places but had a clear preference.

In those days my brothers and sisters were my best friends. Actually, my brothers were my closest companions because my sisters were quite young. My eldest brother, Akbar, is three years older than I, and my other brother, Ibrahim, is a year older. My sisters, Homira and Seema, are two and four years younger.

Growing up, I was never alone. We watched TV, played and ate together. My brothers and I especially liked being outside, even when it snowed. Often, we played and bet on marbles (toshla). The aim was to put the marbles in the hole.

One of our favorite games – it was a true passion – was kite flying. Our kites were made of paper and thin wood strips, and we put a special gloss on the strings to make them strong and sharp, so we could fight other kites and cut them loose. But to really show your power as a kite flyer, you had to chase down the kites you cut and bring them home. It was like a marathon, with fifty kites in the sky, some 3000-6000 feet up! If you lost your kite or didn't have one, you could grab a rock, tie a string to it, hold the other end of the string and toss the rock into the air and over the string of another kite. When the rock fell down, you grabbed it and pulled it, trying to pull down the kite or cut its string.

Another fun game was egging. My grandfather had hundreds of chickens on his estate, so everyday there were hundreds of eggs. My brothers and I liked to throw eggs at other people's houses and cars!

We were so close that the three of us got circumcised on the same day! We all had late circumcisions, at ages four, five and seven years old. I still have a picture of us naked, lying in our beds! Muslim boys are usually circumcised at birth. But I was born at home, in my "great" grandfather's house, and delivered without a doctor. A lady who was our maid also acted as midwife and delivered me. My mother told me that shortly after I was born, I slipped and fell and hit my head and stopped breathing for a few minutes. My head was badly bruised. I sometimes wonder if there is any connection between my Tourette's and that early accident. But I was basically a healthy kid, and my Tourette's did not appear until I was well into boyhood.

The three of us went to a big school across the street and down the block from our house. In Afghani schools you start young, as early as five years old. Even in regular schools you are trained in Islamic studies and in secular subjects, and great emphasis is placed on learning the Farsi language. There were hundreds of kids in our school. In each class-room were kids of different ages. In my first class the ages ranged from five to six. In the next class the range was from six to seven.

I was a smart kid, but I hated school because the teachers

were mean and so were a lot of the older kids. It was common to be beaten by the teachers. I remember when I first came to school, I made a mistake pronouncing a certain Farsi verb, and the teacher told me to stick out my hand and close my eyes. I had no idea what he was going to do. Suddenly, I felt an incredible pain in my hands. I opened my eyes and saw that he had hit me with a stick. I started crying, and he said, "If you cry, I'll hit you again!" Of course, I couldn't stop crying, so he hit me ten more times. My brother Akbar jumped up and came to my aid. He started pelting the teacher with marbles. The teacher then beat him too.

These kinds of beatings happened all the time – and still happen today. The teachers were abusive physically and verbally. Sometimes, they would ask you to lift your feet, then would grab your ankles and hit your feet with a ruler or a stick. They wanted to train you as if you were in the army. I had no respect for them. They were worse than the Russians who eventually took over our country!

If you cried in class, the older boys would pick on you during lunch or after school. They mocked you and sometimes beat you up. Often, they took your lunch money. Fortunately, my brothers would back me up as much as possible. They would either defend me or take revenge.

We called Akbar "the king of the playboys." His name means "great one." Even as a kid, he always had lots of girl-friends. Day and night, he was with girls. One time I caught him naked in bed with a girl and told my father. Dad dragged him through the rain back to my other grandfather's house, beat him, shaved his head and told him, "It's time you stop playing around and start going to school!" Akbar was spoiled by my grandmother, the Airplane. She always favored him over the rest of us kids.

We had a big Zenith color TV, and my other brother, Ibrahim, loved watching it. His favorite shows were Indian movies, and he could sit in front of the TV day and night without moving! When he did go out, he made lots of friends, often with kids much older than he. But he was not liked by the Airplane. He always said that it wasn't right that she spoiled Akbar while mistreating him for no reason. To get back at her, he used to steal money from her safe and buy bags of food and clothes, which he would distribute to the poor, like Robinhood! To this day, he still gives away money to people on the street. He is the spender in the family.

I used to watch cartoons, like Popeye and Tom and Jerry. I can still remember the voice of Olive Oil yelling, "Help, help, Popeye!" I didn't know English, put I picked up a few words. Akbar used to tease me for saying, "hilp, hilp" instead of "help, help." My "great" grandfather spoke fluent English, so I picked up a little from him. I loved watching famous singers on TV, especially Ahmad Zahir, who was my father's best friend. In Afghanistan, he used to be as well known and loved as Elvis. We would sing and dance to his music.

My brother and I sometimes played hide and seek with girls older than us. There were lots of empty rooms at my father's father's house. One time a 14- year-old girl and I hid together near one of the back rooms. We were talking softly, but my aunt happened to walk by and heard us through the door keyhole. She looked through the keyhole and saw me lying naked on top of the girl, so she opened the door. We ran, and she chased us into the front yard, where my mother and the girl's mother were sitting having a cup of tea. Upset by our nakedness, they too started running after us, so I ran to our maid, Fatau, who was ironing and sewing some clothes. She grabbed me and said, "What's wrong?"

"I'm naked, I'm naked," I said. "My mom wants to kill me!"

"What did you do?" she asked.

At that moment, my mom burst in and said, "He was naked on top of Elia, and trying to have sex with her!"

17

"So what, it's free pussy! Let him hit it!" Fatau said, defending me.

"Don't tell my son this. This is bad. He's too young for what he did. I'll punish him for that."

"He's just a kid. He doesn't know better," Fatau replied.

"I will deal with him later," mom said.

Fortunately, mom never punished me! Of course, I didn't know what the hell pussy was. I was just doing what the girl told me to do. I was just a kid.

Chapter 2
The War that Changed
My Life Forever

On the day that changed my life forever, I was watching TV with my brothers. It was about 9:30 at night on December 25, 1979. In a couple of weeks I would be eight years old. We were lying on a big red Persian rug on the second floor playroom of my "great" grandfather's house. It was a big room that could hold 150 people. On the rest of the floor were a kitchen, bathrooms and many bedrooms. We were watching an American cartoon and eating vanilla Afghani ice cream (Jala) when suddenly we heard a big explosion that seemed to come from far off, almost like the sound of a racing car. At that moment, my grandfather happened to be walking by with a book in his hand. I turned down the TV and asked him, "What was that horrible noise? Where is it coming from?"

He said, "Son, don't worry. It's probably a company building a new building."

It was close to our bedtime, so my parents told us all to go to bed. Normally, we got up early, but the next morning I awoke extra early, around 5:30. Since no one else was awake, I went into the playroom, flipped on the lights and turned on the TV. In the middle of watching a cartoon, probably the Road Runner, I heard a loud explosion that sounded as if it were just outside the house. It was so powerful that the house shook.

Immediately, I ran to the master bedroom on the second floor, which has many windows facing the street. Looking down on the street, I saw people running and falling. It gave me goose bumps. To the right I saw a small group of Afghani soldiers with bayonets running toward a tank that was heading in the direction of downtown Kabul. Suddenly, there was an explosion in the street, and when the smoke cleared; I saw dozens of people piled on top of each other – dead and dying people! It must have been a missile fired from the tank. I was frightened, horrified.

As I continued to watch, I saw a pregnant lady, dressed in traditional clothes, running. She was holding a little girl by the hand. The girl slipped, and when her mother turned to pick her up, the whole family was run over by the advancing tank! As the tank passed, I could see only blood everywhere. I can still see this terrible scene in my mind's eye as if it had happened yesterday.

Then I saw a jet plane fly very near our windows – yes, a fighter plane passed just a few dozen feet above our roof. The whole house vibrated, and I heard people in the street shouting, "The Russians are attacking! Mujahadeen, Allah Akbar!" I didn't know what Russians were, but I knew that "Mujahadeen" means "Freedom Fighters." I could also hear my grandmother shouting, "Mujahadeen, hurry, hurry!"

I wanted to see more of what was going on so I ran up to the third floor roof. From there I could see there were several jets flying back and forth. Our driver Mustafa came up on the roof after me, but when I turned around to look at him, I saw him shot down by bullets from one of the planes. His blood splattered all over the roof wall. Mustafa lay dead. He was only nineteen or twenty and was one of my best friends!

Quickly I left the roof, closed the door behind me and

ran downstairs to the second floor, where I hid in our big bathroom. I felt both dazed and terrified as I sat on the stone floor. The whole thing seemed like a dream. To muffle the terrible sounds, I put a wash bowl over my head that was normally used for washing up before prayers. The bombing sounds were so loud that I could hear them coming up through the toilet water. After ten minutes or so, my grandfather came by and led me and the rest of the family downstairs to the kitchen. Many years before, he had built a secret basement below the kitchen. It was a small room but had a few couches as well as a little food. Grandfather cried when he heard about Mustafa. We stayed in the hideaway for two days. At times we heard steps above our heads as the Russian soldiers entered our house. All of us would shake, and as we looked at each others' frightened eyes, thinking these might be our last moments of life, we tried to stifle our tears.

Much later, I found out that the soldiers were looking for men and boys. They would ask you if you were communist or Mujahadeen. If you were communist, you joined them; if you were Mujahadeen, you were sent to jail or killed on the spot. Many boys were sent back to Russia to be trained as army soldiers.

After two days grandfather opened the door. It was the middle of the night. He arranged to have one of his old servants drive us to our other grandfather's house. He covered us with a carpet, so we wouldn't be detected.

My other grandfather's house was like a military fortress. It had dozens of underground passageways and secret rooms, most with reinforced doors. There were even hiding places in the walls! The house was stocked with guns, and many soldiers were present. We had a relatively safe place to hide-out, but dad's parents were incredibly uncaring toward us and decided to leave Afghanistan with their other children but without taking us and one of dad's brothers.

In another two days, my "great" grandfather came to get

us. It was about 3:00 in the morning. He was wearing a beautiful suit as well as a long coat! Yes, even in war, he was immaculately dressed! He kissed us all and gave each of us hundreds of dollars. When we asked why he wasn't joining us, he said, "I love you guys, but this is my country. I will come after I sell my business."

Grandfather had arranged for a driver to pick us up. My family piled into the big, yellow Ford. We were joined by dad's brother, his wife and their newborn baby. So there were eleven of us in the car!

Our car joined a long cue of cars all heading out of Kabul toward Pakistan. The Russians had given the people a choice: to stay and be killed or to leave for Pakistan. We and thousands of others followed the Russian tanks, who were leading us toward the border. It was bumper to bumper traffic, and still dark outside, when we began our journey. As we drove along, we could see Russian soldiers killing kids and men as well as raping women. It was a terrible situation that I will never forget!

A few days into our journey we came upon a long bridge, several miles long, suspended across two mountains. Thousands of feet below were water and rocks. We were the fourth car behind the Russian tanks. Just as we were about to reach the other side, I heard an explosion behind us. It was a rocket launcher firing at the bridge – probably fired by Mujahadeen trying to stop the Russian tanks. Instinctively our driver sped up, so we made it across the bridge, just as it was falling down. When I turned around, I saw cars and people falling to their deaths!

After driving for a few minutes, we came upon a yellow school bus. Inside the bus were Russians dressed in Afghani clothes. They must have been trying to fool the Mujahadeen forces. Without warning, we heard gunfire above us. It was the Mujahadeen fighters trying to stop the Russian tanks. They shouted to the Russians leading us, "Give our people up, or we will kill you all."

A Russian army translator yelled back the reply, "What do you want?"

The Mujahadeen said, "Release our people and fight like men. If not, we will kill even our own people. We will not let you cross this mountain."

The cars in front of us started to move fast, and we quickly followed them. Immediately, a huge gunfight ensued, but we were able to clear out in time. After driving for ten minutes, we were stopped by a Russian tank parked at the side of the road. There were dead bodies all around the tank. Obviously, the Russian soldiers had shot some of the Afghanis that were thought to be Mujahadeen.

Everyone got out of the car except me. I was terrified and hid in the back seat under a pile of clothes. But I decided to peer out the side window to see what was happening. Both of my parents were waving white flags made of towels as my dad shouted, "We are not killers. We are not Mujahadeen." The soldiers made my dad, his brother, and our driver get down on their knees. The driver had a beard that resembled those worn by the Mujahadeen, so they shot him in the head! They also made my whole family get on the ground and started kicking my dad and brothers.

Suddenly, I felt something hit the wheel of our car, and the explosion sent the car flying into the air. The next thing I remember was being in another vehicle. I must have been unconscious for a long while. When I awoke, I felt dazed and weak. My parents began feeding me Fanta soda because there was no other liquid left! Evidently, a Mujahadeen rocket launcher had hit our car, and I had been knocked unconscious. The Mujahadeen were probably trying to hit the Russian tank. I learned from my parents that as a fight broke out between Mujahadeen and Russian forces, dad had found a man with a large van to take us. When I became conscious, I saw dozens of people in and on the van! People were hanging on the bumpers, and I was sitting with my family on the roof rack! So much yelling and screaming was going on around us. Sometimes, I can hear those shouts still echoing in my ears.

As we were driving, a tank came toward us on the one-lane mountain road we were traveling. The van swerved to the edge of the road and almost fell over the side. The irate driver told all of us to get out of his van. Dad offered him lots of money to let us stay with him, but he refused.

My family and many others continued the journey by foot. At times my parents had to carry me. For a week we walked with almost no food or drink. In the middle of nowhere we finally came upon a house where a man and his brother lived. Dad paid him to let us stay a couple of nights. The greedy man also managed to steal some additional money from us. Early the second morning we decided to leave. As we were walking from the house, we saw a tank approaching, but we just kept walking toward the tank because there was no choice. When we reached it, the soldiers started searching us. But in the middle of the search, they received a call and quickly cleared out. What a miracle!

We walked for several days until we finally found a rickshaw driver. Dad gave him his last money to bring us to the border. The driver pulled me, dad and my brothers into the rickshaw and put mom and my sisters on a donkey.

A week later we arrived in Pakistan. I was shocked to discover that dad's father was already there, waiting for us in a big station wagon. He hugged and kissed us – despite his having abandoned us! After leaving Afghanistan, he had come straight to Pakistan and gotten a big house there. Dad was angry with him for deserting us and didn't want to stay at his house. Without money or a place to stay, we were forced to go a refugee camp in the outskirts of Peshawar, a few miles inside the border.

The refugee camp was a hell hole. It sat in the middle of

a desert, where the temperature rose well over 100 degrees. There were flies and scorpions and snakes everywhere and very little food and shelter. The water trucks came every morning, but the water tasted terrible, like chlorine. Thousands of refugees slept in raggedy tents. Because people were poor and desperate, you were constantly in danger of being attacked or robbed. Dad carried his gun to keep unscrupulous people from bothering us.

The whole situation was pitiful! This is how our Pakistani brothers treated us! They didn't lift a finger to help their fellow Muslims! Instead, they treated us like dogs and expected us to lick their boots. But Afghanis are proud people, and we would rather die than be humiliated. Yet we were humiliated by these terrible conditions. Even young widows were forced to beg for food for their shattered families.

Dad did whatever work he could find in the camp as well as in the town located five miles away. He could fix most things and was especially good at repairing cars. To get to the town, he had to walk or run. In the winter the rains were heavy, and the ground became a vast sea of mud! We hated the mud, but it would not stop dad from going to work.

After six months in the camp, dad managed to save enough money for us to move out. He gave the money to me to hold as we journeyed to the nearby town. Along the way I discovered that I had dropped the money! We looked everywhere but could not find it. No one was angry with me, but there were tears in their eyes that I will never forget. We returned to the camp for another few months until dad could earn enough money to bring us to the town.

Finally, dad had enough to rent a two-room apartment in the town of Peshawar. It was a dirty place with lizards in the water, lizards in the bed, lizards wherever you looked! And worms too! You could get the worms from breathing in the dust and from walking barefoot. They started out microscopic, but once they got into your body, they could grow as thick as your finger and several feet long. What a nightmare! On many occasions, I can remember worms coming out of my ass! Dad would try to pull them out. If he were lucky, the whole worm would come out. If not, the worm would tear in two, and I'd be left with half a worm up my ass! My parents then made me eat sweets, which would draw the worm back into my intestines. We'd then have to wait another few days for the worm to regenerate before we could try pulling it out again.

As if that weren't enough, we also had lice twenty four hours a day. Everyday you could see a long line of people outside: mother-child-mother-child-mother-child. Hundreds of people all picking lice out of one another's hair, like baboons preening one another! This was quite a change from my spoiled life in Afghanistan! We did have soap, but it smelled so bad that I'm not sure it was worth being clean!

After a week in our new apartment, I became very ill. Indeed, I lost my memory and sometimes could not recognize mom or dad. My parents took me to a hospital about an hour away and checked me in. It was a crowded two-story building with lots of people in every room. The rooms were dirty, and there were insufficient supplies and medicine. The bathrooms were not only filthy but people would line up to use them.

Dad had to work seven days a week to pay for me to stay in the hospital. For a couple of months he and mom visited me four to five times a week. When dad finally earned enough to buy a cheap beat-up car, they came every night, and mom sometimes stayed over night.

I was put on a ward with mentally disturbed kids who sometimes did strange things to me. One kid, whose head was swollen like a softball on one side, used to throw things at me. Another kid, who was missing his left leg, hit himself all day. He also threw things at the nurses and made weird faces at me. The doctors were also rude to me, and it was hard to understand the languages they spoke: Pashto and Urdu.

My memory kept coming and going. At times I thought I had no mother; at other times I thought I had no father. Sometimes I thought I had four brothers, and sometimes I thought I was dead. The doctors believed I was bewitched. Really, they didn't know what was wrong with me but tried to "treat" me anyway. Three times a day, they injected medicine, with a short needle, into my butt cheeks. The pain was excruciating, and it swiftly spread from my butt to my entire body. When dad questioned whether all of the injections were necessary, the doctor said, "Let us fix him – or take him home."

The doctors and other hospital staff were abusive in many ways. They didn't feed me enough food. They called me names. And they gave me terrible showers: dragging me into the bathroom, soaping me down, pouring cold water over me and then wrapping me in a blanket and putting me in bed. Sometimes they tied me down because they were afraid I would commit suicide. To this day, my wrists still hurt me when I try to lift certain things.

The doctors were right that I was suicidal. I felt like I had gone from a war in Afghanistan to another war, another hell hole, in Pakistan, and I didn't want to live any longer or to cause my parents any more stress and grief. So I sometimes snuck into the medicine closet in the middle of the night and ate other kids' medicines. Once I even drank the Clorox that the janitors used to clean the floors. But I never died – only got stomach cramps! When the hospital staff caught me taking other kids' medicine, they beat me up.

On one occasion, after taking others' medicines, I decided I would stab myself in the heart. I took a long knife, but as I was about to bring it toward my heart, my neck and shoulder suddenly began to twitch, and I was unable to kill myself. This was my first episode of twitches. There were only two.

Little did I know how many millions – I am not exaggerating – were to come over the next twenty-five years!

One time a doctor beat me with a stick that left a red mark on my face. When dad came to visit, I said I had fallen because I knew that if I told him the truth, the doctor would beat me later. But dad is a smart man, and he knew that something bad had happened. That night he asked the doctor to sign me out of the hospital. I had been there for almost a year and a half!

When I got home, I was happy to see my brothers and sisters. We started playing as we always had. They treated me as if I were normal, as if nothing had happened. They knew I wasn't a crazy kid. But in my quiet moments, I realized I was watching a war going on inside myself, and I knew I was a survivor.

For a month I went to small school a few blocks away from our house. Although the school had only about fifty students, it was very similar to the way it was in Afghanistan, only worse. The kids and teachers would beat me up, and all of the kids treated me like an outcast. Their parents, most of whom were uneducated, told them they shouldn't play with me because I was sick, ill, dirty, and bewitched. They called me names like "chicken shit" and "camel jockey running away in war." Some even told me to "go back into your mother's hole." As in Afghanistan, the teachers would hit you for mispronouncing words or the letters of the alphabet. Often, I went home with bloody hands from being hit with a stick.

After a month of being back with my family, I started having memory lapses again and was also passing out. This time dad brought me to a different hospital and different set of doctors. But the experience was even worse. I spent two months in this hospital and lost connection with my parents. It was during this period that I developed twitches in my legs that would make me walk funny. They would come and go unpredictably. The Tourette's was starting to take hold, but neither I nor my family nor my doctors knew what was wrong with me. I would not be properly diagnosed for another two years.

When I was finally released, my family had been in Pakistan for two years. Most of that time I had spent in hospitals. Our neighbors thought I was crazy, and one of them falsely claimed that I had threatened to kill people who messed with me. Dad was scared what the police would do to me or the family, so in the middle of the night, we piled into his beat-up car and drove to a train station a few hours away. One of dad's friends had advised us to go to India. After a two and a half day train ride in a crowded and smelly compartment, we arrived in New Delhi, the capital of India.

Chapter 3
India

It was overwhelming to arrive at the New Delhi train station. There were thousands of people everywhere – sitting and laying on the ground, standing, walking, talking, eating, sleeping, dousing themselves with water. Porters with piles of luggage balanced on their heads – and sometimes with one hand carrying two or three more bags! – were weaving through the crowds. I was fascinated by the diverse individuals and all the colorful clothes and hats.

"Why are those men wearing ice cream cones on their heads?" I asked my dad.

"Those aren't ice cream cones, son," he replied, laughing. "They're hats called 'turbans.' Those men are Sikhs."

In the winter of 1981, the year we arrived, India was even busier and more crowded than Pakistan. I disliked both the busyness and the crowds and told dad that I wanted to go back to Pakistan. "No, we're not going back," he said. His friend had told him there was more freedom, more business opportunities and less racism in India. I was soon to discover that his friend was only partially right.

Because we had almost no money, we settled in a very poor neighborhood in the remote outskirts of Delhi. It was a lot like the camp in Pakistan, only cleaner. Instead of tents, we lived in shacks made of cow dung and branches, but it was still hot and dirty and not very safe. An Afghani family living in the neighborhood helped us acclimate, but I felt very disoriented by the new country. I didn't know the religion, the culture or the language. And it seemed like there were animals wherever I looked. Cows wandered the streets and sidewalks and sometimes entered homes. Both wild and tame monkeys could also be seen everywhere. Some monkeys had even been trained to steal money and valuables. Once I saw several big monkeys, like little gorillas, getting drunk! They ran after people who were waving at them or who were wearing red clothes.

For a month or two, dad didn't work. Then he started getting odd jobs fixing things, much as he had in Pakistan.

Soon after arriving in India, I began attending school. It was hard because half of the kids were wearing turbans, and I would involuntarily say little bad things to them like: "Hey, Gandhi, Gandhi!" "Curry smell, curry smell!" "Ice cream cone, ice cream cone!" and "Dark, black, black, black!" They also freaked out from my twitching.

One of my teachers was a fat Afghani woman, named Mabuba, who practiced the kind of beatings I experienced while living in Afghanistan. She was also scary looking and used to hit me when I mispelled a word. She would say, "You're wrong. Stick out your hands." Then she'd hit me hard.

There were times when I was kicked out of school for weeks because they claimed I was crazy and needed help. The parents of the students started to complain, so I was expelled from the school and sent to a special school. My brothers felt bad about this and wanted to quit school themselves. But I told them, "Please don't quit. I love you guys and will be alright in the other school." My brothers loved and respected me and were willing to do anything to make me happy, even sacrifice their lives, but I didn't want them to quit school.

When I arrived at the new school, I just wanted to die. This school was in a three-story dilapidated building with muddy floors and almost no windows. They gave us no food or water. And worst of all, the school had all the crazy kids. They looked like they wanted to kill you, and most were on drugs. Kids would stand up in class and piss out the windows, which often didn't have glass. Everyday there were fights and theft. Basically, my previous school had lied. This was really a mental hospital, not a special school.

When dad saw that there were so many crazy people, he asked me, "Are you sure you want to stay here?"

"Please get me out of this place as fast as possible before I die," I replied.

"Son, let's go home," he said.

After awhile I tried to go back to school, but they wouldn't let me return. During that time I became very depressed. Once dad saved enough money, he took me to the hospital to get some tests. I still had the same main symptoms: forgetting, blacking out, dizziness, difficulty with focusing. Occasionally I had twitches in my legs.

The big beautiful green hospital was about an hour and a half by rickshaw from where we lived. For two weeks I took tests. They indicated that I needed to be hospitalized again. This time I was fortunate to have a nice doctor, the first kind doctor I had had in two years. He was a six-foot Afghani man. He knew my family had no money and would not let us pay for the medical treatment I received. He also assured me, "I'll try to find what you have." Finally, I felt I was in good and capable hands! He was so generous with me that he even took me to breakfast everyday and bought me the best egg omelets I've ever tasted.

Unfortunately, after a couple of months, the hospital wanted me to have an Indian doctor. They seemed to think that Indian doctors were superior to Afghani doctors. They probably didn't like the idea that our doctor was paying our bills. I was sad when he had to stop caring for me.

The Indian man who replaced him was arrogant and cold and spoke Hindi with a strong accent. I was just starting to learn Hindi, so I had a hard time understanding him. He wanted to do all kinds of tests. I told him that they had already done most of those tests. He said he was a different doctor and needed to do them. I thought he just wanted to make more money. At that time India had the reputation of having the best medical technology and the best fees.

My parents came to visit me once or twice a week. Once again, the hospital staff treated me poorly, very much like the hospital staff in Pakistan. This time, however, I wasn't given many injections. Instead, I was given various medicines and massages, but they didn't help much. I was also put in a neck brace and had to take various stamina tests on walking machines. Because dad's payments were sometimes late, the hospital staff would often hold up my treatments and even deny me food. "No money, go home," was what some staff told me. They also said, "Camel humper, go back home."

For over a year I was in and out of the hospital. At home there were few opportunities to have any fun. I spent my days watching lizards walk on the walls and ceiling of our hut. The lizards and snakes even got into our well water. Though I did play a little soccer, I had the misfortune of kicking the ball into my brother Akbar's nuts. He was hit so hard that he needed surgery!

I had plenty of misfortunes myself. On one occasion when I was living at home, my parents asked me to go to the store in New Delhi to pick up some groceries. At most grocery stores in India, they don't give you a cart or a bag. Usually, you bring your own bag or just hold things in your hands. I didn't bring a bag, so I had to carry several items in my hands. As I walked toward the owner, I suddenly began twitching. He freaked out and accused me of being on drugs and trying to steal from him. I was on drugs: the medicine the hospital had given me!

The police came and arrested me, and I spent several days in jail. They put me in a cell with many people, both old and young. We were fed bread and butter and had to sit on the ground. When we had to piss or shit, the guards would give us two minutes to go out into the alley, where there was a filthy toilet. If you didn't finish in time, the guards would come after you with a stick and hit you. Several guards even beat me! And I was only ten years old.

One day, about six months after arriving in India, I was walking home from school when suddenly I felt a terrible pain inside my jaw and soon wasn't able to open it; nor could I turn my neck to the left. I was all alone, about a half hour from home. Not knowing what to do, I sat down on the side walk and started to feel like I was going to pass out or like someone was drugging me. Then I started to cry very loud, but in the neighborhood where I lived, Lajpat Nagar, no one would come to help a stranger because everyone was afraid of being written up in a police report or a hospital report. So for over four hours I just sat there until my dad and brother found me. They later told me that when they found me, I was lying on my back with my eyes open and staring at them but unable to say a word.

My family immediately took me to the hospital. After doing some tests, the doctor told my parents that because I had been twitching so much, a nerve had locked on the left side of my neck and jaw. The doctor's assistants put a neck brace on me and gave me some shots to help the nerve. Over the next several days I got worse and worse. One doctor told my dad, "Your son has a pinched nerve in his brain. We need to do surgery."

Dad looked at him in disbelief and said, "I don't know, I

don't know. I'll have to think about it."

Several weeks passed, and dad decided that he didn't think the surgery was necessary. Besides, he didn't trust the doctors in India or Pakistan. He hoped that I could get better treatment in America. For several months he had been applying for visas to the U.S., and at last they had come through. When dad returned to the hospital and told the doctor that he didn't want the surgery done, the doctor started abusing me, saying I was a coward and would probably die if I didn't get surgery. He also made other derogatory comments. Dad was so offended by the way the doctor treated me that he knocked him out cold! We then fled the hospital.

Fortunately, we had our plane tickets, and the very next day – early in 1983 – we were on our way to America. All of us were excited to be going to America. We knew it was the land of the free and the brave, and a country of real prosperity and opportunity. We also knew that many different races and cultures lived in America and that it was more accepting of foreigners than were other countries.

Our jet was flown by Japan Airlines. While flying over Japan, the plane hit a terrible storm and suddenly plunged down, down, down. Everyone was freaking out and throwing up, and we all thought we were going to die. Though I was terrified, I secretly felt happy that I might die. I had had enough traumas in my short life. I was tired of spending most of my days and nights in hospitals, surrounded by doctors and nurses who abused me. Miraculously, the plane righted itself at ten thousand feet, and we landed safely in Japan.

At the airport the authorities detained us, thinking we were illegal aliens trying to sneak into America. It felt as if they were holding us hostage – but admittedly, we were pampered hostages! They sequestered us in a fancy hotel near the airport and fed us great food while they interrogated the whole family. We were supposed to stay confined to the hotel, but on the second day dad left because he wanted to see if he could make some money fixing things. The authorities gave him a hard time for leaving and almost arrested him. But after four days of being detained, we were finally allowed to continue our trip to America.

Chapter 4
Coming to America

Our plane touched down at San Diego International Airport. What a thrill to be in the United States of America! So much of my childhood had been shaped by the American shows I'd seen on TV and the American music I'd heard on the radio and records.

Two of dad's brothers were at the airport to pick us up. They were driving a 1978 Toyota pickup truck with a camper shell and made us all climb onto the truck bed. Some welcome! They didn't even bother to put down any carpets or cushions.

An hour later we arrived at my grandfather's house. Yes, the bald son of a gun had made it to America two years before us! He had a big house in Mira Mesa and drove a big car. When we entered the house, it was like entering a zoo: there were his sons and daughters lying around on the couches. I wasn't too happy to see any of them, nor to see my grandparents. They had never been good to my family.

Dad had managed to save $1,400 from his odd jobs in Pakistan and India. It wasn't much money to start on, but I always appreciated how hard he worked for us! After two weeks, my grandfather kicked us out of the house, and dad rented us a little house for $700/month in El Cajon City, a relatively poor and crowded neighborhood about twenty minutes by car from Mira Mesa. The house had three bedrooms and one bathroom, the nicest place we'd lived in since being expelled from Afghanistan.

But after a few days we felt like we were being attacked again by the Russians. As we were sitting at our dining table, a Dodge Ram van drove right through our living room and landed in the neighbor's backyard. Soon the cops arrived and parked outside our house. They ran through our living room into the neighbor's backyard and pulled guns on the van's driver and his partner. After a few minutes we discovered that they had robbed a bank. In a couple of hours a diesel-powered tow truck arrived and backed into our living room! The driver attached two clamps on a hoist to the van and pulled it out of the yard and through our house. Our house looked like it had been bombed.

My uncles got us a nearby hotel room where we could stay while the house was being fixed. Fortunately, the expenses were paid by the landlord's insurance. The night after we arrived at the hotel, I was standing with dad on the balcony as he smoked his cigarette. Suddenly, we heard gun shots and realized it was a drive-by shooting. This confirmed that we were indeed living in a crazy, crime-ridden neighborhood.

After three weeks the rehabbers fixed up enough of our house that we could move back in. It would take another three months before the whole house was repaired. The place was filled with mice and cockroaches. It seemed that every time you opened a door, a cockroach would come out.

Dad soon went to work as a dishwasher at a gyros restaurant about a mile away. It was a famous restaurant open 24 hours a day. People would line up at every hour to buy a mouth-watering gyro. Dad earned minimum wage (about $3.35/hour), so he had to work long shifts to cover our family's expenses. I can remember many times when he would get up at 3:00 in the morning and wouldn't return until 3:00 the next day! At first he used to walk to work, but after a few months he was able to buy a used bike.

After settling into our house, I began attending school a few months. I was not a big hit! Indeed, I felt like a total geek. I had a terrible haircut, terrible clothes and terrible shoes. My hair looked like a wild, curly Afro, and my toe nails were black and dirty from walking barefoot and in sandals in Pakistan and India. All my parents could afford were cheap Wrangler's blue jeans from K-Mart and ProWing shoes from PayLess.

I was now 11 years old, but was placed in the fourth grade. I didn't want to go to school because I knew the kids would make fun of me. I would've made fun of me too because I was so geeky-looking. Dad was dressed also like it was the 1920s!

Dad and his brother took me to the first day of school and brought me to the office of one of the school officials. He said, "Go to class!"

I was baffled and annoyed: "go" means "shit" in Farsi. I looked at the guy in disbelief. He repeated, "Go to class." Again, I just stared at him but was starting to get angry. Why is he telling me that I'm shit? Does he want me to take a shit? Finally, I turned to my uncle and asked him why this jerk keeps calling me a shit? My uncle burst out laughing and then explained that the guy was just telling me to go to class. He also told the official what had happened.

I felt awkward and self-conscious in class. During the second class period, a beautiful girl came up to me and said, "Hi, how are you?" I didn't know what to say, so I just imitated her.

"Hi, how are you?" I said with a big smile. At the moment, I also twitched! It was a terrible neck twitch, the first of its kind that I'd experienced.

By PE class, the twitching started to intensify, and the kids began making fun of me. Within a few days, the twitches involved my fingers, and it looked as if I were flipping off people with the middle finger of my right hand. I also had a twitch in my right eye that looked like I was winking. One beautiful blonde girl told her older boyfriend that I'd flipped her off and winked at her. He was a tough guy who thought he was one of the prettiest boys in the school. To me, he looked like a faggot. As I was walking toward the track field on my way home after school, he jumped me, and he and his friends beat the hell out of me and put me in a metal trash can. They put the top on and then started kicking the can. I was really scared and started crying. When finally they let me go, I left my books there and ran home. Dad asked me what had happened, and I told him I'd gotten into a fight.

In Afghanistan people don't flip each other off with their middle finger. I had picked that gesture up from the American kids. One feature of my Tourette's was, and still is, that I involuntarily imitate the negative behaviors, words and gestures of the people around me. At that time, however, my Tourette's had still not been diagnosed.

Sadly, I can say that I was treated worse by American kids than by Afghani, Pakistani, or Indian kids. They were also worse than my doctors. On one occasion a group of older guys ganged up on me and hit me with baseball bats and balls. Another time four guys clobbered me, ripped my clothes and tossed me into a garbage can.

Within about six months my twitches had intensified to the point where they were occurring on the right and left sides of my neck and in my fingers. My parents and grand-parents were regularly going to the mosque to pray for me. They were also inviting to our house priests from all kinds of religions to see me, hoping that some of them could help. My syndrome had become so well known that everybody in the family and many people in the neighborhood were trying to seek help for me.

On one occasion, one of the prayer leaders from our mosque came to visit me. He was a man in his 40s with a beard and glasses. He talked fast, like an auctioneer. Turning to me, he said, "This is curable. You have to have your mind focused."

Suddenly, I said in Farsi, "Suck my dick, shut up!"

"What did you say?" the man replied.

"Shut up, fuck you, faggot! Shut up, fuck you, faggot!"

Then dad, who was sitting next to me, said to the man, "This is what I was trying to tell you. My son has problems."

The man turned to me and said, "I'm going to give you something. It's not medicine. You're going to get cured, but you have to do what I tell you." He reached into his pocket and pulled out a plastic bag with pieces of paper the size of fingers. Muslim prayers were written on each piece of paper, and all the words were highlighted in yellow.

The man continued: "Take one paper a day, throw it in a glass of water and drink it. And everyday when you take a bath, put a piece of paper in the water, and then throw the water over your head. Do this for 30 days, and you will never see this sickness again."

I was skeptical about his remedy, but for two days, I did exactly what he said. Miraculously, the twitching disappeared and the cursing diminished for about 24 hours. But then I began to get very tired and stopped following the instructions for the next four days. Then I went back to following the instructions, but the symptoms started returning.

In another few days the man telephoned, and dad explained what had happened. The man said, "If your son doesn't continue doing what I said for 30 days straight, then he's not going to get better." When dad told me what this man had said, I stopped believing in him and following his instructions.

Shortly afterward, dad introduced me to an older Afghani

man who prescribed a similar procedure. I thought it was a joke. I didn't believe in him either; I only believe in God. Sometime later, I heard that this old man had cured an 18-year-old American girl who was paralyzed for life. Out of gratitude, she became his girlfriend. What a scandal: the old man was married!

My Mexican neighbor told me about a Mexican lady she knew who had cured many people. My neighbor believed in this lady's healing powers. One day she and her daughter took me to the neighborhood where the lady lived. It was a Hispanic ghetto with lots of gangs. We drove up to a small house with barred windows and entered a small living room with twenty or thirty people waiting to see the lady. We waited for three hours before our turn came and then entered a small dark room.

The lady healer was short, chubby and in her mid-40s and was dressed like a gypsy woman. My neighbor's daughter also had a medical problem, so she lay down on a small bed. While she was lying there, the lady looked at me and said some words in Spanish, which my neighbor translated: "You stand up in front of me."

When I stood in front of the lady, she reached in her pocket, pulled out an egg and pointed it at my head. Then she said some Spanish words that I did not understand. She started saying them faster and faster and suddenly stopped. When I opened my eyes, I saw her sitting on the ground, putting eggs around me in a circle. She then stood up and said other words as she was holding another egg toward my forehead. Suddenly, she hit me in the head with the egg. I freaked out.

In response to my agitation, she said some more words that my neighbor translated: "Don't move. I'm looking for the devil in the eggs."

I continued to freak out. In my mind, I was saying, "Devil in the fucking eggs?"

The lady spoke more words, which my neighbor translated as: "Don't move. Just stand there for two minutes."

I didn't move. Indeed, I watched as she began to work on my neighbor's daughter. She held an egg in her hand on top of the girl's chest. The girl started shaking badly and vomiting. Slowly she began to rise up off the bed and then quickly fell back! The lady started slapping her, and the girl woke up and said, "What happened?"

I was in shock. I had never seen anything like this in my life.

Once the girl got up, the lady said, "That's all guys. You can leave now."

The lady then turned to me and said some words, which my neighbor translated: "Before you leave, take one of these eggs. When you drive out of here a mile or two, stop and get out of the car and throw the egg as far as you can. Also, before you leave, drink this juice that I'm going to give you." She handed me the juice, and I drank it. It tasted like orange juice.

We left the house and got back in my neighbor's car. After driving a couple of blocks, my neighbor said, "Johnny, get out of the car and throw the egg. But you have to throw it on the street where there are no cars." I waited but couldn't find an empty street. Finally, I just decided to throw the egg, and fortunately it landed on the street, not on a passing car. Quickly I got back into the car, and we drove off.

A few minutes later I suddenly passed out and next found myself in my bed at home. Dad was waking me up. As I opened my eyes, I asked, "What happened?"

"What happened?" he echoed. "You shitted all over your bed!"

"What?" I looked around and saw diarrhea all over the bed.

Dad was angry with me and said, "You don't believe in your own religion, but you believe in others? At least you didn't shit from the treatment I got for you. But you shit all over from this Mexican treatment. Son, tell me what happened."

I explained to him everything that had happened. Later that day he asked one of his Mexican friends if he knew what kind of orange juice was given to me to make me shit like that. The man laughed and said it was something sold in Mexican grocery stores that was used to clean out your digestive system by giving your diarrhea. After this "treatment," I gave up on "religious" remedies.

One of the most horrific moments of my life was when I went to a psychologist for the first time. Dad brought me to the hospital to see him. The doctor didn't say much to us. Dad had trouble speaking fluent English and struggled to put words together to explain to the shrink what was wrong with me. No matter how hard he tried to describe my condition, the doctor could not understand him. It was hard and frustrating for me not to be able to ask all the questions that were pounding in my head: "What is wrong? What happened to me? What is the cure? Will I be normal one day? What can I do to make it better?" I wasn't able to ask the doctor these questions because I felt so ashamed of my swearing and twitching and poor English. We did have an Afghani translator assigned to us, but it was hard to say what I needed to say through him. I felt lost and thought that everyone, even the doctor, was making fun of me because I was different. I was also ashamed that my dad could not speak fluent English like the other dads. All I wanted to do was run from the doctor's office and hide myself somewhere far away, where no one could see me. But I didn't have anywhere to go.

As usual, the doctor didn't know what was wrong with me. He thought maybe I was scared from the war and was having traumatic flashbacks. He told us that these twitches would eventually disappear and recommended keeping my mind busy by doing physical activities. I thought he was out of his mind. How could I do sports when I was twitching and cursing and calling people "nigger" and "fat ass" and saying "fuck you" and other profanities. Who would play with me? Most of the time, kids would fight with me because I was using all of these bad words. I had to hide myself from everyone so that no one would see and hear me.

As days passed I became more depressed and withdrew myself from people. Often I hid in my bedroom. I would lock the bedroom door behind me, turn off the lights, put the bed cover over my head and sleep the whole day. At night when everyone else was sleeping, I was usually awake and did all of my daily activities. As my isolation increased, my depression became more and more severe. The medications had a major side effect: they made me very drowsy. My family was shocked that an 11-year-old boy could be so severely depressed. They didn't know what to do and so would blame one another for my condition. Mom blamed dad because he didn't know how to fully explain my condition to the doctor. And since the doctor didn't understand what was wrong with me, he probably prescribed the wrong medicine. My brothers blamed each other for not taking me outside to play. They both thought that my staying inside was a major reason why I had become depressed. Today I know that it was not anyone's fault, not even my own. Back then, however, I just didn't know how to handle the situation.

After a month my parents decided to take me to a nearby hospital where they run all kinds of tests, including MRIs. They tied down my neck and hands and feet so I wouldn't move in the MRI, but my twitching and cursing were so bad that it took over two hours to complete the tests. I also found it hard to breathe inside the machine.

After several days of going back and forth to the hospital, I was advised to see a specialist. This man diagnosed my condition as being Tourette's syndrome. Finally, someone identified what I really had! He was a tall, Jewish doctor with a beard and moustache as well as a little hat on top of his head. He was a nice person who clearly enjoyed his work.

But what was Tourette's syndrome? That was the question that everyone in my family wanted answered. None of us had ever heard of Tourette's. Soon we would discover that we all had a long, long way to go to educate ourselves about the syndrome. At the time, the doctor told me it was a curable syndrome that needed some medicine and mind clearing and focusing. He emphasized that I needed to respect the medicine and take it diligently. Unfortunately, I didn't believe him. After years of living with the syndrome, I didn't believe the doctors.

The medicine was called Orap. Its side effects nearly killed me! It made me drowsy and sleepy. I would take it at five at night, and it would knock me out at around nine. It usually relaxed me enough to sleep through the night. In the morning I had the option of taking another pill. I found that if I didn't take a pill in the morning, my symptoms would be even worse. So I would take the morning pill, but it would make me drowsy for the rest of the day. Orap made my brain dumb. I felt like an idiot, a loser, a retard.

Every week the doctor would say, "It's okay. You'll get better. You need to relax." But I wasn't getting better, so one day I finally demanded, "Change it!" He agreed and switched my medicine from Orap to Heldol. Unfortunately, the new medicine would turn out to be even worse! No wonder they named it Heldol!

I left the doctor and went with dad to pick up the new medicine. A few hours after taking it, I felt relaxed. Then, suddenly, there was a numbness in my jaw. I told dad that my face and jaw were feeling weird. He said it was because I'd changed medicine, and assured me I would eventually be all right. I went to sleep that night, and the next morning I couldn't feel my face and my fingers! I screamed, "Dad!" and he ran into my room with the family following him. "What's wrong, son?" he asked. I couldn't even talk or explain what was going on. I just watched him as he looked at my face, and all I could see were tears running down his cheeks.

We went directly to the doctor, who recommended that I take half of the pills instead of all of the pills at once because my body was not used to the medicine. After feeling that numbness, I felt scared and thought I was going to die that very day. The fact that I was still alive meant that God had saved me again.

When I started to get used to the new medicine, I felt a little better and began to talk more to people and to make friends in the neighborhood. After a few weeks I was walking home from school where my brothers used to play basketball. They had just finished playing, and I was feeling so happy that my Tourette's was getting a little better. I decided to race my brother's home but soon after we began running, I felt pain in my right leg and started to walk. My brothers laughed and said, "Stop playing games like this. It's not funny." Then, I felt as if I couldn't walk at all. My left leg was twisted to the left, and my tongue suddenly stuck out like a dog's, and my neck started twitching badly, and I passed out.

When I awoke, I found myself at the emergency room and in a lot of pain. My tongue was out, and I was licking myself on the shoulder, and biting myself, as well as spitting on people around me. My mind was confused, and I felt like I had a ghost inside of me. All I wanted was just to die right there. I was scared to death what would happen to me next. The doctor said that I had taken too much medicine, but I knew I had not taken too much. In fact, I thought he was full of shit for giving me such a strong medicine. I told dad that this doctor is full of it, and he told the doctor to make sure he gave me the right medicine to relax me, not to kill me or cause me terrible side effects. He warned the doctor not to experiment on me as if I were an animal or a machine.

After all of my bad experiences with doctors, I felt that I couldn't trust them anymore and that they couldn't really help me. I became convinced that the only one who could help me was the one who gave me this syndrome, and that's the man upstairs – God. When I returned home, I went without medicine because I wanted to fight the syndrome without medical assistance. After a few days I was in terrible pain, and the twitches got much worse. Without the medicine I couldn't sleep, and lack of sleep aggravated the symptoms. I was in tears and hid in my room from everyone in my family. I told them not to disturb me so I could fight this alone without the medicine. They understood that I was in pain and that they could not have done anything except let me fight the syndrome myself. For three days I went without food and drink. But after days of beating myself up in the room, I couldn't fight the power of the syndrome any longer and had no choice but to go back on the medicine.

When my family saw my room, they were shocked by how much I had destroyed it. There were dents and holes in the walls where I had rammed my elbows in anger and despair. I had pissed all over the carpet and broken the lamp. I had even put the lamp cord around my neck to try to stop the twitches. Mom called our other relatives to show them what I was going through. Instead of feeling compassion for me, they relatives said that I and my family were not welcome in their homes anymore because they were afraid for their lives and their children's lives. They thought I had a witch in me and would try to hurt them. Dad was outraged by what they said and told them off. Out of concern for me, he decided to stop his relationship with his family. I felt terrible: I was the real problem and wanted to die so that everyone could be happy without me.

Heldol made me more than drowsy. It made me feel like a different person. I was like Dracula, who can't be in the sun. If sunlight hit my eyes, I would scream. Bright light burned my eyes and gave me migraines, so I wanted to hide in the dark. Dad darkened my bedroom by covering all of the windows with heavy curtains.

I literally spent years in my room. It was like living in a dungeon. Sometimes I would stay in the room for four to ten days straight, and dad would call the school and tell them I was sick. The school seemed okay with my being absent – that way they wouldn't have to deal with suspending me for getting into fights. Some of those suspensions lasted for two or three weeks.

Originally, my brothers shared the bedroom with me, but after awhile they couldn't handle being in the dark day and night. So dad put extra beds in my sister's room for them. Sometimes Akbar and Ibrahim would sleep there, and sometimes on the couches in the living room.

While alone in the room, I often thought about killing myself. At times I would try to accomplish this using a rope. Many times I attempted to choke and hang myself with the cord used to tie my Afghani gown but was always unsuccessful. Once I drank my dad's cologne, but all I ended up with was a pain in my belly button, and when I pissed and shit, it hurt a lot. It was like having a Jalapeno pepper in my dick and ass. Another time I drank a whole bottle of Listerine, but only got diarrhea. Once I even added Clorox to a bottle of Windex. Though I felt dizzy for two days, and my balls were numb for two weeks, I somehow still lived!

My brothers, especially Ibrahim, tried the best they could to help me out. Since Ibrahim was good at school, he often did my homework for me or showed me how to do it. I was good at ironing, so I would sometimes offer to iron his pants and shirts in exchange for him doing my homework. It was a nice exchange: he looked good, and I passed my courses! Ibrahim also tried to build up my self-esteem. He would tell me, "You're not a retard. You're not a nerd. You can do lots of things!"

Often my brothers compelled me to come into the living room to play football with them. We had a little football and would do slow motion moves, and when we tackled each other, we'd fall on the furniture and floor. We also played cards with fake money. My brothers wanted me to get my mind off of my troubles and to get stronger. But after a few minutes of playing, I would run back into my room, glad to be back in my den.

My sisters were also good to me. Homayra, who is a year younger than I, didn't care what I had. She just wanted me to be relaxed. We played games like hide and seek. Whenever I found her, she'd cry like a baby and say, "Go start over!" It always had to be her way. Many times she would draw funny things to make me laugh. She also showed me magazines with pictures of Indian movie stars. She loved to collect these magazines, and dad bought her one magazine every week.

My other sister, Seema, who was four years younger than I, was my best friend. She cracked jokes, made funny faces and wore weird masks. She was chubby herself but was forever making fun of fat and skinny people. A naturally happy kid, she had a talent for making fun of the people who picked on me. She would say to them, "Look at yourself. Have you ever seen yourself in the mirror?" Sometimes she would tease me, saying, "Who are you going to bite tonight?"

Everyday my mother was at home, and I could smell the food she was cooking: chicken kabobs, spicy rice, roasted lamb, broccoli with sauce, and lots of garlic and onion aromas. I could also overhear her talking on the phone, telling her aunts and uncles and cousins that I was going to grow up and do better one day. At meal times she would knock on the door and bring me food. Sometimes she stayed in the room and talked to me for hours. She told me what I was like when I was born and when I was a kid playing with other kids and how she would weave clothes while watching us. Each day she wanted me to get some fresh air, but I didn't want to cooperate, preferring to stay in my room. Most days she prayed with me and for me and gave me love. She prayed silently in her heart but sometimes would turn to me and say, "I know you are going to get better. I pray for you everyday. You will get better. This condition is not as bad as you think. We will fight this together!"

Occasionally mom brought the phone into my room so that I could talk to my cousins. They told me about how they played video games, went to the movies, dated girls and had lots fun. Each time I spoke with them I wondered if I would ever be the same as they. It made me sad to think that my cousins were enjoying themselves everyday while I was suffering everyday. After awhile, my mom saw that the calls were depressing me more than cheering me up so she stopped bringing the phone into my room. In those days I badly wanted to visit Disneyland, but I didn't make it there until I was in my twenties and married!

Heldol was a nasty medicine. It even messed up my tongue and made me lose my appetite. The only thing I really enjoyed was pizza, so every night dad brought me a cheese pizza. Many nights dad would sleep next to me and put my head on his chest. To entertain me and cheer me up, he told stories from his life. As a kid he used to like to light things: candles, campfires, house lights. He also talked about the days in Pakistan when he made a car leak oil and almost got killed. His customer didn't pay him for some car repair work, so dad got mad and took the oil out of the engine. The next day the guy came and paid and asked dad to deliver the car to him. That evening, dad drove the car, forgetting that it had no oil. Once he hit the mountains, the car caught fire and blew up. Then he had to work hard for many months to pay back the guy for his destroyed car.

One inspiring story that dad told was about a one-eyed boy from Afghanistan. At that time dad had his business transporting cars back and forth between Afghanistan and Germany. One day, one of his big trucks broke down, and he had a hard time finding a mechanic who could fix it. After some investigating, it appeared as if it were going to cost dad thousands of dollars to get the truck repaired. That same day, an Afghani boy happened to walk by and notice that dad was having trouble with his truck. The boy said he would fix the truck in exchange for some food. He was an orphan who was nearly starving and had never been given a chance to prove himself. Dad's partner was suspicious of the boy and thought he just wanted some free food and wouldn't be able to fix the truck. But dad believed in the boy and wanted to give him a chance. With dad's consent, the boy climbed on the truck, and within several hours completely fixed it – without using any tools! After telling me this story, Dad looked into my eyes and said, "Son, you're just as good as that boy."

Dad never made me feel stupid or bad and always encouraged me to be strong. Some days he forced me to go to work with him, instead of going to school because he knew I did better when my mind was focused on something. He also knew I preferred to focus on his work rather than on my school work. After leaving the gyros restaurant, he had gotten a job at a car dealership washing the cars. It was a small dealership with 50-60 cars that was owned by a Persian man. Dad told the owner that he used to fix and sell cars, and the owner said he needed another salesman and encouraged him to get a sales license. Dad quickly became a very successful salesman and made lots of money for the dealer.

On the occasions when I managed to go to school – which was less than half the time – there was always someone to torment me. At age 13 I was put into regular junior high classes with normal teenagers who had no clue what was going on with me. They didn't understand what Tourette's was and so were mean and rude to me. The boys always wanted to fight me and beat me up. They made my time at school hellish by constantly making fun of me and showing no respect for my syndrome. They belittled me with such names as "camel humper," " camel jockey," "drug lord," "camel balls," "camel licker," "fucker," and "jackoff," and they often told me to "suck a camel," "go camel ride a pony" and "get fucked." And because some of my symptoms made noises, they would say "the vacuum cleaner is here" and "the chicken man is here." These kids used more curse words than I did!

Everyday seemed like a battle day. One day at school, when I was in my PE class, our coach told us to play softball. As usual I was sitting on the bench and waiting to get picked by a team but was not chosen. I was left alone while the kids started to play the game. Suddenly, five minutes into the game, one of the girls got hurt and could not play because of a minor injury to her finger. There was no one else to bat, so they had no choice but to pick me to bat for her. While I was batting, the coach told the pitcher, Billy, not to pitch the ball while I was twitching. But Billy was one of the kids who always picked on me. He waited for the moment my twitching began and then threw the ball toward my head. As I turned back to hit the ball, it hit me in the face. I was immediately dismissed from the game and sent to the nurse's office because the ball bruised my eye very badly.

When I got home from school, I told my dad what had happened and that I didn't want to go to school ever again. Being from the old school, he did not really understand me. He said, "Son, look into my eyes. You're the son of an Afghan warrior who left everything behind back home and brought you kids here to have a better life. Now, do not be weak – be strong, you could overcome this." While he was saying these words to me, I saw tears filling his eyes. I understood his pain from struggling in this country with the language and with the financial difficulties of raising a big family. He had been the son of a rich military man; now he was having a hard time making a living. I felt his pain and promised that I would be stronger, and would never let him down. I said I would go to school and bare the pain and not disappoint him again.

Unfortunately, my vow to be stronger didn't make the situation at school any better. Although I started feeling stronger emotionally, the others students didn't leave me alone to concentrate on my studies. They would start something with me in order to cause problems.

One day, shortly after returning, I was in the stairwell, walking up to the second floor just as another student, a black kid, was walking down the stairs. Suddenly, my twitching kicked in, and by accident, I bumped into the kid, and he dropped his books. Immediately I said I was sorry, but he ignored my words and began calling me names. When I said, "Don't call me names," he started punching me. He was a tough boxer, almost like Mike Tyson, so I could barely fight back. Not only did he give me a swollen eye, but he also knocked me out. When I finally came to, my brother Ibrahim was kneeling near me. I told him what had happened, and he decided to take revenge. He was the strongest kid in middle school and usually acted as my bodyguard. Quickly he tracked down the kid and beat him up.

Though I hadn't started the fight or even wanted to fight, I was suspended for two weeks, and Ibrahim was suspended for a week for helping me. The kid who started it all didn't get suspended at all! He lied to the principal, saying that I had attacked him and that he was just defending himself. The principal didn't want to listen to me or my brother. He didn't like having my syndrome in his school. I remember sitting in the principal's office and putting ice on my eye as he explained that he was going to suspend me and Ibrahim. The principal was a tall, mean mother fucker. He seemed to think he was a tough FBI agent just because he carried a walkie talkie.

Shortly after returning from the suspension, I was outside playing four square with another boy during first period. I hit the ball hard, and the boy hit it back hard to me. Back and forth the ball went. Suddenly, the boy got belligerent and threw the ball in my face. Some of his friends saw what was happening and joined in. They punched and kicked me. In the distance I could see that the principal was watching us. He approached me and grabbed me by the arm and said, "Let's go inside!" The way he grabbed me as well as the sound of his voice told me that again I was going to be blamed. Once in his office, he called my dad and said, "Pick up your son, Mr. Bahar. We can't have him here. He just got into another fight." So I was suspended for another week!

On another unlucky occasion, I was sitting in class during second period. My Tourette's twitching kicked in, and I began repeating names like "bitch, bitch." The guy sitting in front of me, a tall black kid, turned around, thinking I was bad mouthing him, and socked me in the left eye. He continued to pummel me with his fists, but I couldn't fight back because I was stuck in the seat. I pleaded, "Please, you don't understand. I don't mean it." But he wouldn't listen. The teacher, a short chubby bitch, who looked like a parachute, was of no help. Instead of assisting me, she dismissed me. I arrived at the principal's office crying and bloody and already knew what was going to happen – another suspension!

The suspension took place a day before my 14th birthday. It was not a happy day! I had invited my relatives and a few kids to my party, but no one showed up! The only ones there were my immediate family. I became convinced that no one would ever like me and care about me, so later that day I went into my room and took 14 codeine pills. I was amazed when I awoke the next morning and found myself still alive!

The school year is about nine months long. With all of the

suspensions and illnesses – which caused me to miss 7 to 12 days of school each month – I was in school for only about four months! However, with Ibrahim's help and with some of my own effort, I was able to graduate junior high school.

I remember well those last weeks before graduation. After so many suspensions, I was very stressed, and the whole school was getting on my nerves. All I could think about was the promise I'd made to my dad and to myself to not give up on school and not let the war at school defeat me. The final tests were scheduled for just before graduation. I was told to go and take my test at the principal's office. I went there and for a whole week took the tests. When the day finally came to receive the graduating grades, I returned to the principal's office and complained to him that I would not graduate this year because he had suspended me so many times. I said I was very mad at him and at the teachers and kids, and it was not fair how I'd been treated at this school. He looked at me and said, "Listen, kid, here's your final test grades. You've passed all your tests. Congratulations to you – you've made the freshman class."

Wow, was I surprised! And I was so happy that I couldn't wait to go home and tell my dad, "I love you! I made it! There is hope after all!"

Before going home, I went to tell the other kids at school, especially the one kid who always picked on me, that I had graduated. Unfortunately, I wasn't aware that he had failed the 8th grade. One of my happiest moments got quickly ruined when he hit me so hard on my chest that I couldn't even breathe. It was stupid of me to tell him about my happiness after all he'd done to me. He seemed happy to hit me hard. But while he did hurt me physically, I realized that he'd gotten hurt even worse by failing.

After passing the tests and getting beaten up, I went home and told my parents that I'd passed the 8th grade. They were so happy! They wanted me to always pray to God and always be strong in life because it's all a matter of how you handle things in your heart.

At this time I had no friends. Indeed, lots of kids preferred to make themselves into my enemies. Even my neighbors were against me. There were several 12- and 13-year-old boys who lived in the houses behind ours. They used to beat me up and steal my bike. One night my dad had to call the cops on them because they were throwing eggs at the house.

I still felt incarcerated in the house. If I went outside, I was sure to get my ass kicked. From ages 11 to 15, my life was pretty much homebound, or rather, room bound.

Chapter 5
My High School Years

My high school years, from ages 14 to 20, were the worst years of my life. The high school kids were older and tougher than the middle school kids, which meant I got beat up more frequently and fiercely. The school was also very crowded, and Tourette's doesn't like crowds. Crowds quickly trigger the syndrome.

During the years I went there the high school developed a terrible reputation. At one point dozens of teachers and students were busted for drug dealing. The cops even found drugs hidden in the classrooms! Kids from different races, ethnic groups and economic classes attended the school, but it was run by the rich and middle class kids. Poor kids, like me, were treated like dirt.

Of course, sometimes the minority kids picked on each other. One day when I was in woodshop class, a black kid standing near me spit a loogie on the back of my neck. "What the hell!" I said. "What's your problem?"

"Nice shoes, ProWing Sir," he replied. ProWings are the cheap gym shoes that I wore. My family couldn't afford to shop for expensive shoes, so I had to settle for dorky shoes bought at PayLess.

"Watch it you black monkey ass nigger," I blurted out. That was where I was wrong – but it was too late! The kid hit me behind the neck with a piece of wood. Then another guy came around and socked me in the jaw, and I fell to the floor. Another kid kicked me in the face and pulled off my shoes. He put the shoes in the wood-cutting machine – and suddenly it stopped. I screamed for help, and the teacher, who had been at the other end of the room helping the girls, finally came over to us. He was a fat, mean man who talked like he was in the army. He looked at the stuck machine and said, "Boy, what in the hell are you doing?"

"I got beaten up by these guys," I replied, "and they put my shoes in the machine."

The teacher stopped the machine and picked me up and said, "Get the hell out of my class, you sick animal!"

I left the class bleeding and without my shoes. I went straight to the principal to complain about how I'd been treated. Instead of sympathizing with me, he suspended me because I'd called the kid a "nigger."

Four days later, I returned to school. During lunch, the same group of guys that beat me up in woodshop again clobbered me. This time, however, my brother Ibrahim stepped in and defended me.

A little later that day, a tall Hispanic kid came up to me and said, "You got balls? Be a man and meet me at the field to fight." He explained that the black kid from the woodshop had told him that I'd called him a "wetback." I said that wasn't true. But he insisted that I meet him outside on the field, so I had little choice but to agree.

Ibrahim accompanied me out to the field. "You're not going to fight," he said, so I hung back. The Hispanic kid had brought along his older brother. He attacked Ibrahim and pulled his hair, but Ibrahim knocked him out. The younger brother insisted on fighting me, but I didn't want to. Some kids standing nearby shouted, "Fight, fight!" and then pushed me into fighting. I barely got a punch out before being knocked out. The kid sat on top of me and socked my face twenty or thirty times. While this was happening, Ibrahim was held by five Hispanic guys. I got the beating of my life. My face was almost unrecognizable.

The principal eventually arrived and – you guessed it – suspended me for two weeks. There had been witnesses to attest that I was innocent, but none of them dared to come forward because they were Hispanic gang bangers.

Dad was appalled by the damage done to my face, so he went to school and filed a report. Of course, the school didn't do anything! The principal called a meeting, but the other kid's parents didn't show up. The only ones at the meeting were me, dad and the principal. The principal said, "I'm sorry, sir, they're right. Your son is the cause of all these headaches. They don't have to show up. They rejected you because of what your son said. Please take care of your son." Dad was so angry that he wanted to hire a lawyer to sue the school, but he didn't because he had no witnesses who would talk.

Though I had a couple of friends at this time, I had trouble maintaining the friendships. Once I went to a friend's house, which was located near a train station. His parents got mad at me for cursing, so they turned to their son and said, "Why did you invite this kid here? We told you he is sick and that you might catch his sickness." Then they kicked me out of the house. I was really mad and felt totally worthless. As I approached the train station, I decided to jump in front of the train. But as the train was approaching the station, I suddenly heard my dad honk his car horn. He had come to pick me up. He told me to get into the car and saved my life.

A few months later, I went again to this same friend's house. Hoping to get his sympathy, I told him that I'd tried many times to kill myself yet had never died. This friend, who was not really a friend, said, "Here, take some of my dad's blood pressure pills. You'll be knocked out." When I did take them, I got very high and passed out. Four hours later I awoke, and my "friend" was surprised that I was still alive.

When I was 15, dad decided to use his savings to purchase a car dealer's license. He had some bad experiences working for other dealers and thought it was time to own his own dealership. He rented a small house that could be used as a business, put a few cars in front, and started fixing and selling used cars.

A month after the dealership opened, we moved to a nicer neighborhood, the Spring Valley section of San Diego. I still spent a lot of time in my room. From the window I would watch children playing and would often wish I were as normal as they were, so I could play too. Until then, I had always thought that a miracle would happen and make me normal again. But as time passed, and the miracle did not knock at my door, I would fall into despair and depression.

To try to pull myself out of the depression, I would have various conversations with myself in front the mirror that was in my closet. Sometimes, I would say to myself in the mirror, "Fuck you, asshole, you should be out there playing with all those kids. They look worse than you. One's got freckles. One's got an Afro. One's got his pants backward. You shouldn't hide in the dark because of your syndrome. I'm gonna be stronger. I'm gonna be stronger. I'm gonna be stronger. I'm gonna beat you!"

Unfortunately, after saying all this, I found myself back in my room watching the same kids. The self-talk didn't work very well!

Hope is a strange thing: it can cause relief and stress. My constant wondering when my syndrome would go away was a regular source of anxiety. When you feel hope, it's easy to get frustrated and sad whenever your hope is defeated. The increased frustration and sadness can make you even more depressed. And, of course, giving up hope is also very depressing because life seems bleak and not worth living. I can't even count how many times I wished I were dead.

Tourette's was not something I had created purposely, nor could I get away from it. It was something uncontrollable, something like a monster inside me which made me make only enemies, not friends. From now on, I would work around it and against it.

Dad tried to help me out by insisting that I sometimes join him at the dealership. When I wasn't at home, I split my week between school and work. I discovered that I had a talent for both selling and fixing cars. In a good month I sold twenty to twenty-five cars even though I was cursing and twitching the whole time! Once I remember twitching while I was reparking one of the cars: the steering wheel turned, and the car hit another car's bumper! Fortunately, I could also fix cars! I repaired engines and put in transmissions and kept my mind busy.

Unfortunately, I still had bouts of deep depression. With all of the suspensions from school, I thought I should just die, so one Friday after school I drank two bottles of my mom's nail polish remover. My eyes turned red, and my tongue got numb, and I felt high. Yet I survived!

I did my first year and a half of high school in San Diego. In the middle of tenth grade, we moved to the San Francisco Bay Area. In both locations I had bad experiences with the teachers. My relationships usually started out positively, but most of the teachers couldn't handle my Tourette's symptoms and eventually turned against me. I guess it's hard to blame them. I did some disturbing things, even if they were done against my will. It was hard for teachers to handle me repeating things like: "I fucked you in the ass. I fucked you in the ass," or "Suck my dick. Suck my dick," or "He raped me. He raped me." The Tourette's also made me throw pencils and papers at the teachers. When I walked by one fat, ugly teacher, the Tourette's made me pinch and slap his butt! During a test, when all the students were quiet, I sometimes started repeating, "I cheated, bitch. I cheated, bitch," or "I copied Henry. I copied Henry." Several teachers made me write on the blackboard a hundred times, "I will not do this again while in class with teacher So-and-So." I'd also have to write this sentence several hundred times as homework.

You're probably wondering why I couldn't just stop the Tourette's symptoms or program myself to say something nice rather than negative. Well, I ask myself that question every day – yes, every day. I talk to my Tourette's and try to convince it to say nice things and stop saying nasty things, but it doesn't listen. It's like somebody else is living inside of me with his own mind and will and telling me what to say and do. I've tried prayers. I've tried meditation. I've seen priests and professionals. I've told Tourette's, "Enough is enough! How about if we switch the words and become different and become a different person. What if I shut my mouth for one minute and not say either 'ee ee' or 'fuck you.' What if I could make it two minutes?" But it was all to no avail.

I know that what my Tourette's says or does is often terribly upsetting. Who am I to tell people to stop being upset? The only thing I can do is tell them, "This is my handicap. If you accept who I am and what I do, then fine. If you don't accept me with my handicap, then I'm sorry, you must move on without me."

During my whole time in high school I was shuffled back and forth between regular classes and special education classes. It's not that I couldn't do the work in the regular classes; it's more that the teachers didn't want me in their classrooms. I felt like a pingpong ball being knocked back and forth. The principal would send me back to the regular classes when he saw that the Special Ed classes were too easy for me. But then my Tourette's would get me in trouble again, and I'd be sent back to the Special Ed classes.

Initially, I resisted going to the Special Ed classes because I felt I was smart enough to stay in the regular classes. I just had Tourette's, not a learning disability. But the principal insisted that I go.

It turned out that the times I spent in those Special Ed classes were the high points of my high school career. Most of the kids had Down's syndrome. Some had other severe psychological and physical problems, like distorted bodies and lopsided faces. I loved those kids and learned a lot from them. They were so sweet and innocent. I remembered looking at them and looking at myself and saying to myself, "Gosh, I got Tourette's. I get beaten up. I get thrown out of school. I get suspended. People treat me like shit. But these kids have even more problems than I have." This realization made me sad and yet thankful for what I had.

These kids had no friends except each other. I quickly got attached to them, and they got attached to me, and soon I wanted to help and guide them. In fact, I made it my job to assist them. I used to take them to the bathroom and wait for them. Some were in wheelchairs and needed special assistance. Others needed help washing their hands. Many of the kids were afraid of getting lost, and some got picked on by the regular students. I tried to teach them to be strong.

I felt closer to these kids than to anyone else in the high school. It brings tears to my eyes when I think about how much I enjoyed being with them and how much I miss them. We studied and played together. I even joined them in their PE classes. When we played softball, they didn't know how to hit or to run to first base, so I showed them how. They made fun of my twitches, but it didn't bother me because there was no malice in it. They would also curse when I cursed, but again it was all in good fun and not to put me down. There were times when they got angry at the teacher, and I stepped in and calmed them down.

I remember a little Chinese boy named "Lee" that I used to play with. My Tourette's would call him "Cous Lee," which means "Pussie Lee" in Afghani. He used to stand there unable to move his arms and legs very fast. He walked like an old man and looked like he always wanted to do some form of martial arts with me. He loved to talk and would never shut up until you said, "Shut up." Then he'd say, "Okay!" and would stop talking. He loved food, especially vegetables and fruit, so I often brought him carrots and bananas from home. I would bring enough for the two of us, and we would sit down and eat together in class. He was my buddy.

Some of the kids had special talents, not just special needs and handicaps. There was a very talented Italian boy who could beautifully and accurately draw your face in less than ten minutes. His handwriting was also very beautiful.

I had my best learning experiences with these handicapped kids. Six or seven of us would sit around a round table and answer questions together. We would share different ideas and see who was right or wrong. I really enjoyed studying with them. If I hadn't become close with them and gotten to love them, I probably would have been an asshole to them the way the other kids were – the so called "normal" kids.

The special education teachers were awesome. In fact, with two exceptions, the only teachers I really liked were Special Ed teachers. They were not offended by my Tourette's. They understood I wasn't saying and doing things on purpose. It goes to show that people with understanding and compassion can help all kinds of people. These teachers loved doing things with the students.

One of the sweetest teachers was a big guy, 6'11", with a beard. He taught English as well as basketball. He was very polite and loved to help everyone in his class. He was so helpful that he made you fall in love with his English class! I had fun in his classroom. He told me, "Say what you want." What a relief to not be censored for everything I said! He set up a basketball tournament for the handicapped kids, and then invited the whole school to it. He was a tremendous teacher and person!

I had a beautiful math teacher – not a Special Ed teacher – who was in her early twenties. She was so gorgeous that all the guys wanted to "attack" her. She was also very accepting and playful with me. When I cursed at her, she cursed back at me – with a smile! She had fun with me, and if the other students objected to my behavior, she said, "If you don't like it, go to another class." I wish there were more teachers like her! It is great to be around someone who understands and appreciates you – and who is willing to stick up for you.

During both my middle school and high school years, I had some unofficial teachers who taught me more than the official ones: they were the African American brothers who played basketball everyday from 3:00 to 9:00. I used to sit and watch them play. I studied their dribbling and shooting. I studied their moves and fakes. These guys were great players. They ranged in age from 20 to 60, and many of them could have made the NBA if they'd been given a chance. I watched them for months, absorbing everything I could.

One day they were short one guy. I heard them talking among themselves, "Hey, let's get this kid that's sitting there … Get him and throw him the ball. Let him do whatever he wants. At least we'll have a guy to play 5 on 5."

Then one of the players looked over at me and said, "Hey!"

"What?" I said.

"We want you to play with us."

"Why?"

"We need you to play a full game of 5 on 5."

I was nervous and hesitant, but I went onto the court. They tossed me the ball, and I started dribbling. But as one of the opposing players rushed at me, I threw the ball away. He said angrily, "Mother fucker, keep dribbling on me! Don't throw it away when I'm coming at you!"

So they threw me the ball again, and I started dribbling. And that's how they taught me to play the game. Whenever I dribbled wrong or shot wrong, someone yelled, "Stop the game!" Then they'd give me back the ball and ask me to do it right. Every single one of those guys showed me how to play the game, and I eventually became a great player myself. In a few years I became a quick mover, fine ball handler, tough on defense, and with a great shot. I could even consistently sink the 3-pointers.

Eventually I became so much a part of their group that they called me "nigger." During a game they would shout to me: "Hey, nigger, shoot the ball… Hey, nigger, pass it here… Hey, nigger, I got your mother here." Yes, they taught me to talk and swear like them. They were my best teachers of English and of cursing!

They also taught me to be strong. They showed me how to box and to walk and to take off my shirt. They even stood up for me when trouble happened. One day while we were playing, some guy stole my bicycle, which was parked near the court. The brothers knew who the guy was and where he lived. They turned to me and said, "Go get your damned bike and be a man!" Then they led me to the guy's house, which was located about five blocks from the basketball court. With them standing on the sidewalk behind me, I went up to the door and knocked. The guy came out and said in a loud vice, "What do you want?" Then he laid into me with a string of curses. Immediately, my friends grabbed him and beat the hell out of him. They went into his house, retrieved my bicycle and also took some of his possessions, which they threw on the front lawn.

What's also amazing is that the brothers knew what Tourette's is. When I told them I had it, they said, "My sister has it," "My uncle has it," "I got it, fuck you." Evidently, it was very common in the African American community. Most people knew someone with Tourette's or had heard about it on TV. To this day, I find African Americans more accepting of Tourette's than any other race. One of my African American clients recently said to me, "It's a free country. Everybody curses. Call me whatever names you want. Even the president curses. As long as you are who you are helping me with my shit, that's all I need."

Despite my good connections with the brothers, I still struggled with depression. Shortly before my 16th birthday, I attempted suicide again when my dad's family called me a "loser" and said that a diseased person like me who curses all of the time shouldn't be brought into their house again. I took the entire bottle of Heldol. It must have contained at least 17 pills. I went to sleep and awoke the next day. I felt high and couldn't see well, nor could I feel my balls.

A few months after my birthday, one of my neighbors made fun of my Tourette's and beat me up really badly. I went to my house and cried and took 13 Tylenol pills and drank my dad's whiskey. I went to sleep and awoke the next day tired but alive.

Another suicide attempt occurred shortly after this. I was with my family at the beach. We were playing volleyball with some people on the sand, when suddenly this older guy asked me to get off the team. He said, "We're losing because of you. Are you on some kind of drug? You twitch too much and can't control yourself enough for this volleyball game. So go swimming, little guy."

I got really mad at him. Though I didn't know how to swim, I walked to the ocean and went into the deep water over my head. I started drowning, but someone pulled me up by my hair and shoulder and saved me. I survived again.

It was always hard meeting new people and making friends. Once dad invited his friend over to our house. The man brought his two teenage daughters with him. I thought, "Here's an opportunity to make some new friends." But the first thing out of my mouth was, "Nice daughters! Cute pussy, pussy!" The father freaked out. My dad tried to calm him, saying that I had something given to me by God. The father calmed down, but I could see he was still pissed inside. And I never became friends with his daughters.

We moved to the Bay Area in 1989, when I was 17. The first place we lived was an old house in Union City. Dad had been ripped off by his family in San Diego and only had $6,000 in cash left plus two used cars, some furniture and other accessories. We rented the house from an Indian man for $1,000/month. We came to the Bay Area to be near my mother's brothers, but they turned out to be almost as unhelpful as my dad's family. Mom's younger brother had a car dealer's license and had recently taken over part of an Oakland dealership owned by Iranians. My uncle said that dad could share some of the dealership space that he was renting. There was only room for dad to park six cars. They were cheap cars, ranging from $300 to $2000. Dad bought them at the auction, fixed them up and then resold them. The place was so small that dad literally had his office in the bathroom at the end of one of the hallways. Customers came into the bathroom and signed their contracts while dad sat on the toilet – fully dressed, of course!

In the first month dad made a good profit! I helped him buff and detail the cars and quickly became an accomplished detail man. We would buy a car at the auction for, say, $700, fix it up, put a sign on it for $2,995, and sell it for $2,500 – making a healthy profit. The second month was great too. Unfortunately, my uncle got jealous and decided to kick dad out of the dealership.

Dad decided to get his own dealership, a small place in Oakland. He sold a few cars but didn't do particularly well. Then he heard about a place in San Jose. It was an old tattoo shop that could fit only four cars. Dad decided to give it a chance. Within a year, and with the help he got from me and my brothers, he grossed a satisfactory income.

When I was 17 and living in Union City, the school authorities wanted me to go to a special school. It was a house that had been turned into a school for kids who were having trouble. You went to school for an hour, picked up your homework and then brought it home. After a few weeks of attending this school, I said, "No, I'm not going to go here anymore. I have Tourette's, but I want to graduate from a regular high school with a high school diploma."

"You can't do that!" insisted the principal. "There are too many issues, too many problems."

"No!" I said, and was sent back to my regular high school.

I was nineteen when I made my last suicide attempt. I drank three bottles of whiskey and two bottles of wine and smoked a pack of cigarettes. Yet I survived once again. After all of these suicide attempts, I realized I was a very strong kid! No matter how strong the pills, I would never die until God called me to him. I was so relieved that I was alive.

Now, when I look back at what I did, I am shocked that I am still alive and surprised that I have made it this far. I am lucky I did not damage my kidneys or liver or skin. I was so depressed and stressed with this syndrome that I figured I would do whatever it took – suicide or hiding – to get rid of it. But I can see in retrospect that Tourette's has made me strong in life. It has shown me how to be a nice person in public and elsewhere. It was stupid and selfish of me to try to kill myself, but I learned from the experience and decided to never do it again. The important thing is to learn from your mistakes.

During the middle of eleventh grade, we moved from Union City to San Jose, where I went to three different schools. From eleventh grade on, I started to get out of my house more often and to play basketball everyday. I had simply gotten tired of hiding out from the world in my room. At first I played basketball with my brothers and their friends, but as I became more skilled, I played with lots of different players.

I remember one day showing up at a court near my house. There were players there of all races and nationalities: black, Indian, Mexican and whites. One of the teams picked me, and everyone was surprised by how good I was. That day I was unstoppable. I was on fire. Even when I was twitching, I could still pass and shoot. One of my specialties was fade-away shots. I averaged 16 points a game – out of 21 possible points!

It actually took me six years to complete high school. In the last couple of months of my senior year, the principal said I had to go to a certain school in San Jose. That school was known for having lots of druggies, gangsters and low-income kids. Again I refused to go. I told the principal, "You are going to give me the final test when the day comes. I am going to prove to you that I can take them faster than anyone and can pass them and get my diploma and get the hell out of high school!"

Nineteen ninety two was an important year in my life. On May 13 my dad came into my bedroom at night as usual and said what he always would say, "Take your medicine, son."

But instead of taking it, I said to him, "You can stick the medicine up your mom's ass!"

He looked at me in surprise and then suddenly threw the medicine against the wall. "I just stuck it up my mom's ass!" he said with a laugh.

Together, we cleaned up the mess. From that day on, I have never taken any medicine for my Tourette's. This is what God gave me, and this is what I have.

I finally graduated from high school in 1992 at age twenty. What a triumph! I felt good about myself for having survived all the craziness and suffering and managing to get my diploma. But I didn't feel good enough to attend the graduation ceremony because I knew the kids would made fun of me. I had also never attended a single high school dance.

Chapter 6
Tourette's Self-Employed

The week before graduating high school, I'd gotten my car dealership license with the $8,000 that dad had loaned me. I started with four cars. At first, I lacked confidence and was unsure if I really wanted to own my own dealership. When I'd sold cars for dad, I'd experienced a mixed response from his customers. Some of his customers hated me for cursing and even filed law suits against dad. Other customers admired me and said such things as, "Your son is so motivated. I wish I had a son like him." After working with dad for several years, I concluded that I was probably doing him as much harm as help. The main reason I got my own dealership was to spare him the stress I caused by pissing off his customers. I remember one time when an overweight man came into the dealership to buy a car. As soon as I saw him, I kept saying, "Fat fuck, fat fuck, Shamu, Shamu! You can't fit in this car! You can't fit in this car!"

He got mad and said, "Why are you calling me fat you little skinny fuck? I should beat the fuck out of you right now."

"Come on fat ass, come on fat ass!" my syndrome said. It also made me make faces at him. I tried to explain that I

73

had Tourette's.

"Fuck your Tourette's," he said and started to chase me. Incidents like this convinced me to move on.

Before getting my own dealership, I tried many times to get sales jobs at other dealerships, but my swearing inevitably got me in trouble, and the end result was that I was always quickly fired. One time I kept repeating, "Shut up, shut up!" to one of the dealers as he was asking me some questions.

He got incensed and shouted, "You shut up and get the hell out of here!"

Dad helped me to get my dealership going. He helped me purchase some cars and initially assisted me with some detailing. Then I was on my own. Within a few months I was starting to do well. Within five years I had over 200 cars and great credit and was known by all the auctioneers. At the auction I bought 30-40 cars at a time and settled quickly.

It's strange, but my customers loved my cursing. Why? Because I decided to take a new approach with them. I realized that the reason others had disliked me for cursing was that they didn't understand why I was cursing. I decided it was best just to tell my customers about Tourette's before they even opened the car door. What I discovered was that if I got into conversation with them, they wouldn't even listen to the engine. Rather, they would just drive, sign the papers and leave. Most felt bad about what I had gone through and so would just buy the car and go home happy. Of course, I also treated my customers well. They knew that if there was any problem with the car, I would take it back and have the problem fixed or would replace the car. I got lots of referrals from friends and satisfied customers.

My brothers worked for me – Ibrahim full time, and Akbar part-time – and I had a half dozen sales people and several secretaries. Between 1992 and 1996 we did very well. Many dealers in the neighborhood envied my success.

At the auctions I did make lots of friends – or at least, lots of friendly acquaintances. Auction agents, tow truck drivers and secretaries were all nice to me because they wanted my business. I enjoyed seeing them at the auctions but never went out with them to have fun.

In fact, I didn't have much fun at all. I worked seven days a week, usually from 9:00 a.m. to 9:00 p.m. and sometimes to as late as midnight. On Sundays I ran the dealership myself. And for five years I never took a day off!

Why was I a workaholic? To make myself focus. To be a successful business man at a young age. To drive a dream car and wear expensive clothes. I used to wear thousand dollar suits as well as shoes and ties that cost between $150 and $250. But when I became rich, I did not become an asshole. I never treated people with disrespect. I never acted better than anyone. I gave the same heart to everyone I knew. I am a lover, not a hater. To this day, the longest I get mad at someone is ten minutes. Then I say, "Let's be friends." I don't want anyone to be my enemy.

By early 1997 I was totally burned out. I was 22, and all that overworking had run me into the ground and made my Tourette's fly off the charts. Lots of stress, coupled with lack of sleep, is terrible for Tourette's. As the symptoms got worse, they made me hesitant to approach customers and to handle problems that needed my intervention. There were times I even broke down in tears. Tourette's also cost me some additional expenses. I used to stand in line at the Department of Motor Vehicles to get permits and registrations for my customers. But when my Tourette's got bad, the symptoms would scare people standing in line with me. So after awhile, I was forced to hire someone to take care of the DMV work for me.

The used car business is itself stressful. The cars come with no warranties, and if they break down, you have to have them towed and brought to a mechanics shop, which can be quite expensive. Sometimes you pour a lot of money into fixing up a car but then can't sell it, so you have to bring it back to the auction and take a loss on it. The auctions themselves are incredibly competitive. There are days when you get completely outbid by other dealers and come back without any cars. On top of that, dissatisfied customers are always suing dealers. So you can see that I had plenty of good reasons to be stressed out!

My Tourette's got so bad that I started not showing up at work. Though I put my brother Ibrahim in charge, he had gambling problems and was losing my profits. I was forced by my syndrome to close the business and sell my lease, fortunately at a fair profit. Unfortunately, I had to use the profit to pay some debts and had no other choice but to file bankruptcy.

During the time I had been successful, I realized that being successful gives you more stress than being poor! Of course, when you're poor, you are also stressed that you don't have the money rich people have! But on average I think many poor people are happy as long as their stomachs are filled and they're not on drugs. There is an Afghani saying that "the less you eat, the happier you are."

The day after selling the business I went to Las Vegas to chill out and have some fun. But I found Vegas even more stressful. When I was gambling at the tables, my Tourette's would say, "I'm cheating, I'm cheating." It also made me twitch and curse. The casino manager overheard me saying these things many times, and saw that I had actually won a number of games. He thought I was drunk or perhaps actually cheating, so he called security. Three security guards took me to a room and strip-searched me. Finally, I told them I had Tourette's. One of the guys knew what it was, but no one believed I had it, so they told me that if I gave back my winnings, they wouldn't call the cops. I wasn't feeling strong at that time, so I returned the money, and they told me to leave. That is why I hate Las Vegas and will never go there alone.

Not only was I distressed and disturbed from working nonstop for so many years, but I was also forced to sell my house in Fremont. I moved back in with my parents. For the first couple of weeks, I hung around the house during the day and sometimes went out at night with my brothers and their friends. We visited clubs, drank, shot pool, smoked cigars. I didn't enjoy the clubs because everyone wanted to kick my ass or assumed I was on drugs and would ask me if I had any crack to sell. Soon I got sad and bored of these "boys" activities, so I just stayed at home and watched TV, mostly sports.

I used some of the time to try to figure out why my Tourette's had so flipped out. At that time I was getting intense twitches in my left shoulder and making loud noises and screams. While hanging around the house, I learned that I could control the symptoms if I stayed away from people, relaxed in the backyard and focused my mind.

For almost a year I stayed at home. I would go outside mainly to walk in the neighborhood and play basketball. On the basketball court, the other players would laugh at my swearing. But they used to curse so much themselves that they weren't bothered by my words. Mainly, they had to accept me because I was a great player. I played guard, inside, outside, and would often sink the three pointers. In fact, if I'd been in better shape, I probably would have made the NBA. In my whole adult life, I never lost a game to anyone. To this day, I still play smart and tough. Sometimes I twitch, and the ball hits me in the face, but I quickly get the ball back.

To get back on my feet and make some money, I began working for a Nissan dealership in San Jose. My brother Ibrahim was working there and he talked me up as a great salesman. I didn't tell the management I had Tourette's because I knew they wouldn't hire me. So I got the job and then tried to hide my syndrome. On my third day, a Chinese client came in with his wife and kid. He wanted to test drive a car. My Tourette's soon started acting up and saying, "Fuck Chinese! Fuck Chinese!"

The guy turned red with rage and said, "Fuck you, fuck you, you mother fucker! Get your boss. I no fuck Chinese."

I said, "No, sir, you don't understand. I have Tourette's."

"Fuck you!" he said. "I no carrots."

He kept cursing me and then went into the showroom to get my boss. He told my boss, "He keep saying 'Fuck Chinese.'"

The guy was really belligerent, so my boss kicked him out of the dealership. But then he took me aside and said, "Why do you curse like that?"

Trying to cover my ass, I said, "I didn't."

After a couple of weeks, it finally came out that I had Tourette's, but I was such a good salesman that they decided to keep me. In fact, I became the closer – the one who closes the deals. I pushed their sales up with my sales technique. As before, the secret of my success was simply looking the customers in the eyes and telling them that I had Tourette's. They would listen intently and would usually want to buy from me. So Tourette's had the power to establish real human connections as well as break them.

In less than a year a new management team was brought in.They fired almost everybody, but Ibrahim and I were kept. We had to endure all kinds of abusive language. They called me "camel balls," and Ibrahim "fat camel." They also cheated us out of some of our salary and commission. I wanted to sue them for the racial abuse, but the lawyer said I didn't have enough evidence of discrimination. Eventually, I just decided to quit.

Reading the newspaper, I noticed that a car dealership was for lease on Fremont Blvd. I drove over there with my dad. I had only $10,000 plus about $8,000 worth of old cars. The showroom could hold only 7 cars and was equipped with phones and desks, but the land could hold another 150 cars. The owner was asking $5,500 per month and wanted a deposit of $17,000 to cover first and last month rent and additional expenses. Dad said to me, "Son, this dealership is too big and too expensive."

I said, "I am going to get it and turn it around and make some real money."

Dad was stressed out by the situation. He was now retired and had lost a lot in some bad business investments.

The dealership owner was a nice guy, and his lot had been vacant for several months, so I decided to offer him $10,000 and my promise that I would pay the rent on time each month. He agreed to a 5-year lease. We ended up getting the place under dad's dealership license, and I became the manager.

I spent a few days cleaning up the lot and then put out a big sign that said, "Consignments Welcome." Then I bought three Auto Traders magazines and started making calls, asking people to bring me consignments. At the beginning, it didn't work. But then I sold my '87 Ford Taurus for a good profit. The next day I sold two station wagons for another good profit. I gave dad some money and told him to purchase more cars at the auction. Then I began telemarketing and was able to sell all cars in one day with a nice profit. After a month, I had 30 cars and changed my consignment fee from $99/month to $399/month. Soon I had 80 cars, 50 of my own, and was as big as a new dealership. I hired two salespeople and in June 2000, with my brother Ibrahim's help, we had huge sales!

There was a Corvette dealership next door to us whose lease just came up. The lease was for $17,000/month. I decided, what the hell, I would get the lease so that I wouldn't have a competitor next door. I came into this business with almost nothing, so I might as well play hard.

I filled up the new showroom, and fixed up the place a bit, but wasn't able to create enough business to cover the additional costs, so I decided to lease out some of the space. On the window, I put a "For Lease" sign that said, "Call John or Mike." "John" is the name I've used in America since moving to San Diego. Mike is dad's American name.

Chapter 7
Married Man

Shortly after placing the "For Lease" sign in our showroom window, I received a call from a woman.

"Can I speak to John, please?" she asked.

"Who?" I said.

"John."

"This is John."

"I'm interested in some property next door. Can you tell me something about it?"

"I'm here for an hour or so. Do you want to come over, and I'll show you the property?"

"Okay. Where is your location?"

I told her I was at the dealership next door.

I will never forget her arrival: it is etched forever in my heart. I was standing about fifteen feet from the entrance to our showroom, which has French doors. I was holding some papers as I talked with a customer. In slow motion, it seemed, I watched a very beautiful woman open the door and saw the wind blow her hair. This hot woman in a fancy skirt and Gucci glasses just walked right through the door and came directly toward me!

"Hi, can I speak to John?" she asked.

"J-J-John. Oh, oh, I'm John," I stuttered.

"Are you all right?" she asked. She seemed genuinely concerned about my stutter.

"Yeah. Do you want to come to my office? I want to speak with you and show you the property."

The instant I turned around and began walking toward the office with her behind me, I bit my tongue and said to myself, "Damn, I'm in love!"

As I walked, I could hear her steps and smell her perfume. Suddenly, I wheeled around and asked, "Are you Persian?"

"No. I'm Afghani."

"Man, even better!" I said to myself. Her body was slim, and her face gorgeous. All I could think was, "When am I going to touch those lips with my lips? I wish you could just sit on my lap and kiss me now."

She told me that her name was Weda Shah and that she was looking for a space where her brother could open his Persian rug store. Her plan was to help him with the business.

As I took her around, we compared observations about our common Afghani heritage. When we got to the subject of Afghani marriages, I decided to try to talk her into going out with me. She told me how marriage screwed up the lives of so many Afghani women. The divorce rate was high, and so was wife abuse. Then I brought up marriage in America.

"Are you married?" I asked.

"I don't date in my culture," she said, emphatically.

I never thought I would be married to her – she was too beautiful. But I kept trying to go out with her, and each time she said, "I don't date."

Dad saw us talking in my office and came in. She introduced herself, and he asked what family she came from.

"From the Adel Shah family," she replied.

"Are your brothers' names Ibrahim and Alam?"

"Yes, how did you know?" she asked, excitedly.

"They are good friends of mine!" he said. "I knew them in Afghanistan. From which mother are you?"

"From the second mother, Aliyah Shah," she answered excitedly. I was later to discover that her father was married to four women at the same time!

I felt happy that dad knew her family. At first, my Tourette's wasn't very noticeable. But as the conversation developed, and we began to talk more about her family, my Tourette's started saying, "Khar cus, khar cus," which basically means "donkey pussy" in Farsi. She freaked out and turned to my dad, saying, "Why is he so pissed off, cursing all the time?"

"He puts too much time into the business. That's why he's so stressed out," dad said, covering for me.

I was determined to be with Weda. Though she didn't want to go out with me, I persuaded her to go to Starbucks for coffee that day. As we sat at a table, sipping our coffees, she told me, "If you are hitting on me, I'm not a whore. I'm not one of those girls who dates. I don't do anything, so let's just be friends."

I looked at her and said, "Okay, let's just be friends, but just give me your number so I can call you back with the lease options."

So I kept calling her for days. One time I said, "I want to go out with you."

"I'm not interested in dating," she replied.

"I want to give you everything! – take my money, take my Mercedes," I said.

"I don't need your money!" she said. "I know about money. I just want someone who cares about me. Go fuck yourself, asshole!"

I hung up and didn't speak to her for weeks. But then I called her back and apologized for bringing up money. Then I said, "I'm in love with you. I want to marry you!"

"All the guys say that," she shot back. "You're all full of shit! Go fuck yourself!"

She was really mean, but I was in love with her and so I persisted. You know what they say about love: when you see it, your heart falls for it.

Eventually, we met again at Starbuck's. I turned to her and said, "Let me tell you something."

"What?" she said. Then added in a softer voice, "Shake my hand first. I want to be your best friend. I never had a guy friend before."

I was touched by her offer, but I said, "I don't want to shake your hand because I'm gonna marry you. I'm in love with you. I will promise to God that I will make you my wife!"

Her mood turned hard again. "Whatever you say, good-bye," she said and took off.

After a week, I ran into her again at Starbucks and said, "I love you. I swear to God." And I kissed her. She was furious.

"I'll tell my brother to kick your ass for what you just did to me," she exclaimed.

"If your brother comes to kick my ass, I'm still going to marry you!" I insisted.

That's when she looked at me and said, "You really love me that much?"

"I feel in love," I replied. "I'm a man, and I fell in love, and I want a kid with you." Then I paused and added, "You know what I want?"

"What?" she asked, with tears in her eyes.

"I want a little girl with curly hair, like the one in my dream, who says, 'Daddy, Daddy,' every day."

"You really love me that much?"

"Yes, I do!"

"Then I want you to do something for me. There's a Koran in my car. Come with me."

We walked outside to her car, a black Jetta. She said, "Sit in the passenger side."

She got into the driver's seat, and I got into the passenger's seat.

"Look into my eyes," she said, "and tell me you really love me."

"I do love you."

"You do?" She paused and then said, "Open my glove compartment."

I opened it.

"Take the Koran out. I want you to put your hand on it and swear to God that you love me."

I put my hand on the Koran and said, "I swear on the Koran that I love you. In the name of God I love you more than anyone, and I want to marry you."

She looked at me and had more tears in her eyes. Then she said, "I believe you." She kissed me. "I'm yours now. You know what to do next."

I was confused by what she meant. I thought perhaps she wanted me to take her now.

"What do you mean?" I asked.

"Duh," she said. "Send your family to come over and ask for my hand."

I was relieved. I kissed her and said, "I gotta work on this right away. I'll see you soon."

That night I was excited. I felt like the world finally realized who I am. I told my dad, "You know that Adel Shah's daughter that you met. She's mine! So go to the house and ask for her hand from the family."

He looked at me and said, "Come on, son, stop kidding around. It's not funny anymore."

"I'm not fucking joking," I said very seriously. "Get the family together and go on Saturday."

"Really?"

"Really!"

He was shocked. Finally, he said, "Okay, son, we will go. But are you still serious?"

"Yes, dad! I will give you the address on Saturday."

It took my family over a month to get her family's consent. They had to check out my character and family background. During those months before our engagement, I was remarkably free of Tourette's symptoms. Weda made a point of looking up Tourette's on the internet, and though she accepted what I had, she didn't fully understand it. Her family finally showed their agreement to our engagement by giving my parents a piece of candy – a sign that the union should be sweet.

As a kid and young man, I never used to eat at restaurants because I was afraid of creating a scene, but Weda convinced me to go to restaurants with her. While we were sitting at the table, I just focused on the beauty of her face and kept my mouth closed – and no symptoms showed up! It almost felt as if I didn't have Tourette's! What a miraculous time that was!

The engagement ceremony took place in her house. We took a beautiful silver platter and covered it with candy, sweets and $2,000 in cash. Weda was dressed in green clothes, and a priest (mullah) was present. Weda's parents set a fee of $300 for the dowry – in case the marriage was broken. Three hundred dollars is the maximum dowry according to Islamic law.

The next day, there were over two hundred people at our engagement party, which was held at a restaurant in Fremont. We had food, live Afghani music and dancing. In our culture, only family members dance with one another. We had a small cake and took lots of photos. I gave Weda an engagement ring, and her family gave me a watch. We had a great time – including the Tourette's, which was acting up badly!

After our engagement, my symptoms intensified again. Often my Tourette's would say hurtful things. One time I was driving by a motel, with Weda at my side. Suddenly, I said, "I fucked the girl at Motel 6. I fucked the girl at Motel 6."

"What the hell are you saying? Did you really do that?" she asked.

"No. Tourette's, fucker, shut up!"

When I was around some of the beautiful women in her family, I'd say, "I wanna kiss her. I wanna do her." I even said to her brother's wife, "O bitch, O bitch." Her family knew about my Tourette's and didn't say anything about my behavior, but I could tell it was hard on Weda.

In the fall of 2000, a few months before our wedding, I quit working for my dad. Weda wanted me to show her that I was an independent man who could support a family. I started hustling: buying and selling used cars. With the money, I rented an apartment in Fremont for $2,000/month. It was definitely beyond my means, but I wanted to show Weda that we would have a good life together.

We were married on January 26, 2001, a year and a half after our engagement, and three weeks after my 29th birthday. The reception was held at a wedding hall in Fremont. It was a plain hall, where many Afghani weddings take place, but I spent over $20,000 decorating the wedding hall, with the help of the whole family, and made it look like the Taj Mahal! I was wearing a tuxedo, and Weda was wearing a beautiful, white, American-style wedding dress. She looked hot!

We had over 350 guests. I was so nervous with all of the people looking at me that my Tourette's went wild! I was twitching right and left and, of course, cursing. It was embarrassing, but at one level I didn't mind because I got the beautiful girl as my new wife! All I wanted to do was take her home and start my husbandly duties!

Of course, Tourette's has played a big part in my sexual life with my wife. It's hard to kiss a guy who is twitching and swearing – let alone make love to him! My Tourette's has a way of shouting indelicacies in Weda's ears: "Fuck me in the ass!" "Fuck me till it hurts!" It also calls out other women's names and even calls Weda names like "fat, fat" and "ugly, ugly" (when she became pregnant). I also make lots of weird noises that don't make much sense. In general, my Tourette's is pretty noisy, whether I'm in bed or anywhere else. Weda can be patient and accepting, but she has her limits.

The first two years of our marriage were tough. I wasn't having much luck selling cars and was almost flat broke except for a few thousand dollars in savings. Weda was going to college, studying criminal justice and planning to become a lawyer. I not only wanted to support her but also wanted to make enough to raise a family soon. Because of the stress, my Tourette's revved up, and I wasn't sleeping well or much. There were times when I didn't make enough to buy groceries or pay the rent.

Shortly after we married, Weda told me, "I want to have a kid."

I said, "Okay." But I was scared for a lot of reasons. We didn't have enough money for ourselves, let alone for a child. And I was afraid that the kid might be handicapped. What if the kid had Tourette's? What if he were retarded because of all the medicine I took?

For months we tried to have a kid. I began to think that maybe the medicines had ruined my sperm. Then, one day, in our third month of marriage, Weda turned to me and said, "I'm pregnant." She had taken a self-test.

"Damn! I'm a father!" I exclaimed. I was shocked and thrilled. In disbelief, I asked, "And I got you pregnant?"

"Yes," she nodded.

I started crying to myself and saying, "Damn! I'm a father! Damn! I'm a father!"

As the pregnancy proceeded, I became more and more anxious about the possibility of my child being born with a handicap. We had an ultrasound test done after a few months, and when I saw the picture, the baby looked like an alien kid without eyes. It was weird-looking, like a blank ghost. I would often be awake in the middle of the night, praying to God that the baby wouldn't have any physical deformities or mental syndromes. Weda was also concerned that the baby might have Tourette's. She would often ask me, "Do you think that God will give my kid Tourette's syndrome?"

"It's all up to God," I would say.

She was confused about whether or not it was inherited because doctors and the internet were giving us mixed information. "God knows the truth," I told her.

On January 30, 2002, a few weeks after my 30th birthday, I had the privilege of witnessing the birth of my daughter. I had driven Weda to a hospital in Fremont. Our doctor was a Chinese man. Weda was lying on the bed in the Labor room, and as she was pushing, the baby wouldn't come out. The doctor told us that the umbilical cord got stuck and that they needed to do a C-section. I was so nervous that my Tourette's said, "Fuck you, Chinese doctor! Fuck you, Chinese doctor!"

The doctor got mad and gave me a dirty look. Then he said, "I gonna cut your wife to get baby out! I gonna do C-section!"

"No!" I said. "We're going to make this baby come out. And there ain't gonna be no C-section!"

The nurses also told him not to do the C-section. One said, "The poor lady is trying her best to get the baby out!"

But the doctor was really annoyed with me because of my Tourette's, and he walked out of the room, leaving Weda with the nurses. Weda pushed some more, and the nurses encouraged her, "Come on, you can do it! Think about something really upsetting!"

When the baby was halfway out, Weda said to the nurses, "Where is the doctor? I know he is annoyed by my husband's Tourette's, but I don't want to be treated inhumanely."

One nurse turned to me and said, "We know it's not your fault." Then one of the other nurses ran to get the doctor.

When the doctor came in, Weda continued to push, and he decided to use a vacuum suction to the head to pull the baby the rest of the way out. She popped out at 9:45 a.m.

I was in shock when I saw the baby come out – and scared. My Tourette's said, "Cone head! Cone head!" Yes, the baby had a cone-shaped head, and I thought it might be retarded.

The doctor said, "Don't worry; the cone will go back down as the kid grows."

I was relieved and began to cry in joy, fear and relief. As they were cleaning the baby, I grabbed her foot, and she looked at me and laughed! I kissed her on the lips and started crying again. We named her Hassina, and the next day took her home. "Hassina" means "beautiful" in Hindi.

In the afternoon, family and friends came to the hospital to see the baby and congratulate us. My Tourette's kicked in big time, and I started saying, "Fuck you, guys! Losers! Suck my dick! I saw a big pussy!" To Weda's brother, I said, "I did her, I did her! I got her pregnant! Touchdown! 10-4!" I also said, "Alien baby! I'm gonna drop you!" Every time Hassina cried, I said, "I'm gonna slap you, bitch! I'm gonna choke you, bitch, shut up!" Some of the nurses became concerned and took me aside and asked if I really had Tourette's or if I was on crack. I assured them I had Tourette's. To one nurse, I kept saying, "Fat ass! Fat ass!" She said, "Whatever, dude" and took off, really pissed off. In reality, I love my daughter to death. I would die for her; it's just "the other me," "my devil twin," making me look like an idiot.

I went down to the cafeteria to get a snack with Weda's niece. When we got to the cashier, who was a Mexican woman, my Tourette's said in Spanish, "Panocha, cayate!" which means "Pussy, shut up!"

The cashier said, "cayate cavron," which means "Shut up, you fucker."

Then Weda's niece, who was only thirteen, turned to the cashier and said, "Shut the fuck up. He has a condition, Tourette's."

As they began arguing, I walked away. On my way to Weda's room, I started yelling in the hallways, "I got fucked in the ass! I got fucked hard!" People looked at me weirdly. One lady said, "Watch the swearing, son!"

My Tourette's said, "Whatever!"

On that day my Tourette's was so bad that I decided I needed to go home and change my clothes. I usually feel more comfortable when I put new clothes on. My Tourette's then starts to relax and subside. So I briefly returned home that afternoon, changed and then came back to the hospital.

The next day, as we were leaving the hospital, I started saying, "Kidnap! Kidnap!" while I was bringing Hassina to the car. The old valet parking attendant began screaming, "Excuse me, sir, who's baby are you kidnapping?"

The security guard heard him yelling and approached me. "Excuse me, sir, can we see some kind of I.D.?"

"Fuck you! Fuck you!" I said.

Fortunately, Weda was at that moment coming out of the hospital in a wheel chair, surrounded by family. "What are you guys doing?" she asked.

"Is this your baby, ma'am?" the security guard replied.

"No, this is our baby!" Weda shouted. "And that's my husband!"

She gave him a dirty look and then explained the syndrome. They apologized, and we got in the car and drove home.

We now had a two-bedroom apartment in Fremont. Our first apartment only had one bedroom, but after six months we'd moved to a larger apartment for about the same price. We put Hassina in the second bedroom, and Weda stayed with her for the first few days. Then Weda's mother, who had been living with her son, came over for a few days and stayed in the baby's room. She supported Weda and helped take care of Hassina.

As a first-time father I didn't know a lot about parenting. But from my dad I learned how to kiss and hug the baby. I was excited to be a father but also anxious that I might hurt Hassina with my twitching. I had to be careful not to drop her! My Tourette's, ever the provoker, would say, "I'm gonna drop you! I'm gonna drop you!" Or when it was feeling really wicked, it would say, "I'm gonna choke you! I'm gonna choke you!"

Hassina slept a lot as a baby. Her sleeping reminded me of myself since as a boy and adolescent I was always on medicine that knocked me out and made me sleepy. At first I was laid back toward Hassina and afraid to touch and hurt her. I also wouldn't sleep in her room because I was afraid I would startle or scare her with the noises my Tourette's made. Though I feared hurting her ears, I would look into her eyes and say to myself, "Is this mine? I did all this? God! I have an angel baby!" Sometimes, when I was feeding her with a bottle, my Tourette's would blow air into her face, and she would almost choke. Then I would turn my head away and hand her over to her gramma or mother because I didn't want to hurt her.

As Hassina grew and grew, I fell in love with her every moment of the day. I prayed to God, "Thank you for the most beautiful and healthy child!"

I believe that no matter whether a person is doing well or badly, he should always thank God. I don't believe in praying just when I'm doing badly. It is important to thank God for both one's poverty and one's wealth. Sometimes, people forget God when they become rich. I think it's important to never forget God and to always thank him for whatever you have or don't have. Many people don't have what I have – a beautiful family. I'm blessed with it, and I appreciate it.

There were times when I felt I wanted to go back to my high school and say, "Look what I have! What about you?"

But I realized that if I did that, then I would just be the same asshole as the people who used to put me down. As it would turn out, people would find out anyway and were amazed by my fortunate situation. Some said, "Wow, what did you do to deserve this?"

In the first few months after Hassina's birth, lots of relatives came to visit us and see the baby. I used to ask my sister why she always hugged her kids so much. She said, "When you have your kids, you'll be hugging and kissing a lot the way I do."

When Hassina was about two months old, I had a really bad Tourette's episode. She just looked at me as if to say, "What the hell is wrong with you?!" It wasn't until she was four or five months that I got more involved with her and held her more. I'd make her laugh by biting her cheeks or neck. But I was still afraid to take her in the shower with me. I thought I might drop her and knock her into the wall. When she turned eight months old, I started to crawl around with her and chase her around the house. Sometimes I'd lie on my back and pretend I was dead. "I'm dead. I'm dead. Somebody better come and kiss me," I'd say, and she'd crawl on top of me and kiss me. From eight months on, Tourette's really didn't interfere with my relationship with her.

Hassina motivated me to work hard for her. If she didn't eat, I would suffer. If she didn't sleep, I would be in pain. If she were ill, I'd cry.

The first months of fatherhood were incredibly stressful. For seven or eight months I had barely made any income. Because Weda was often sick, I had to feed the baby two, three, four times in the middle of the night. The lack of sleep and energy triggered my Tourette's. With more twitching and cursing I was unable to work effectively. To make a little extra money, I started selling my possessions: VCRs, rugs, my car. The infant formula was expensive, and I was still having trouble finding money for groceries.

My mother-in-law had moved in with us when Hassina was six weeks old. This was a great help, but it didn't assist our financial situation. She got social security payments, but I didn't want to take any money from her or from the rest of my family, and besides they were all busy trying to support themselves. Often we lived on tea and bread, and some days Weda was in tears and close to despair.

Weda never forced me to get a job. She would look in my eyes and say, "You are a survivor, and I believe in you. You are going to come out of all of this, and we are going to make it together. And I'll make sure that no one ever harms you again and takes advantage of your Tourette's."

A few days later I found a job at a used car dealership in San Jose. I worked for this Middle Eastern dealership for two months without getting paid. I made over $50,000 in sales commissions. They told me to come back on my day off, and they would pay me then. I found out that they had lied to me and sold the business. I went to their house to get the money, and they told me they had filed bankruptcy.

I was incredibly stressed because I and Weda were counting on that money. There I was again with no job and no money.

Despite our poverty, Weda continued to take care of her relatives in Afghanistan and Pakistan, as well as orphans and widows who lived there. For the past ten years she had made it her weekly practice to take a large part of her income and send it to her impoverished relatives, many of whom would have died without her faithful assistance. Before we married, Weda worked at Saks Fifth Avenue. She made a nice income then, and sent several hundred dollars each week to her relatives. Of course, now that we had so little money, there was hardly anything to give.

But one day I managed to make $180 selling some things. I was planning to use the money for groceries. That same day Weda got a call from Pakistan saying that a man sick with cancer needed money for his treatments and his family. Weda said, "We have to send them the money."

"How about us?" I pleaded.

"We can survive, but they can't."

I thought about it and decided to trust her judgment. I took the $180 to a store in Fremont and had the money wired to the man. As I was driving home, I thought, "Here we are suffering. I'm making a little money to buy groceries, and here my wife is asking me to give the money away." I paused and then thought, "Maybe it's meant to be. Maybe it's meant to go there. Maybe with their prayers and support, there will be more." I was never upset about it because I figured that if I can have one kid, I can have ten. The air and water here are cleaner. Over there, they have nothing.

I guess my wife was blessed by God to do this kind of work. She is a special woman, so special that I don't say "no" to her on these matters. I want to give her my whole power and support. She does the right stuff: many people are alive today because of her. At times, giving money to others almost felt like a sport to me: if we didn't send the money in time, they wouldn't score! Sometimes, it felt like a business, as if I owned a mosque or an orphanage. Because of our efforts, many of those people in Afghanistan now own their own homes.

Still, for the first four months of Hassina's life we had terrible struggles with money. But then Weda decided it was time for her to stand up and help her husband by getting a job. And what a job it turned out to be! In May she met a guy in a mortgage company who wanted her to work for him. In late July she brought home her first paycheck. I was sitting on the couch when she came home. She handed me the check for $25,000! It brought tears to my eyes. Wow! We cried and hugged each other and kissed! I looked at a picture of Mecca that was in our living room and said, "Thank you, Allah, for the biggest check that we haven't seen in so long!"

Two months earlier we had already decided we wanted to move out of our apartment, but the check made the move even easier and sweeter. In fact, instead of lowering our living condition, we decided to raise it. We ended up purchasing a three-bedroom home in the Ardenwood neighborhood of Fremont. We convinced the owner of the house to carry back 15% of the note, so we just put down 5%, and he carried the second note. It was our first house, and the mortgage was $3000/month.

Weda's second paycheck exceeded the first one! We were flying high! Unfortunately, the guy who brought her into the business turned out to be a slime ball: though he knew she was married, he started hitting on her. After a few months he was fired, and Weda began to work with an Indian woman. Weda learned the business quickly and eventually got me involved, knowing I was such a good salesman.

We have tag-teamed for almost five years. As I brought her more loans, our financial situation improved rapidly. Whenever I'd meet someone on the street, I'd ask if they were looking for a house and needed financing.

We worked hard, really hard. Lots of our clients lived in Los Angeles, so we drove down there twice a week, often leaving in the early morning and returning at 2:00 or 3:00 a.m. Driving was a way to save money on airline tickets. In one year we made a healthy profit!

My daughter Hassina taught me how to be a father. She taught me how to love more and play more. She even taught me to be on time because I knew that if I didn't show up, she would cry. When she was just a little girl, as young as a year and a half, she would hold and kiss my neck if I started twitching.

I could see in her eyes that she wanted everything in her life – and I wanted to give her everything, especially the things that my dad couldn't afford when I was a kid. I wanted to be a father who could afford to give her a good life. I didn't want my kid to be laughed at at school for wearing ProWing shoes. When you wear $20 shoes, people think you're a loser. I wanted people to think my daughter was a winner.

Our second child, Husnah, was born in February 2004. Weda had been working all through her pregnancy. In fact, she was working up until the moment her water broke! We called an ambulance to take her to the hospital in San Jose. The doctors and nurses didn't want me to stay in the hospital, but I said I was going to sleep there anyway. The next day, February 2nd, my daughter popped out her little head into the world. I videotaped everything – well, almost everything! When they were cleaning Husnah, she looked at me, and I said, "Daddy's here! Love you!" She never cried!

In the nursery there were lots of Vietnamese boys who were all crying. My Tourette's said, "Shut up, Chinese fuckers!"

A nurse confronted me and said, "Mr. Bahar, you need to lower your voice."

"I got Tourette's," I said.

"I know," she said, "but you have to relax."

My Tourette's didn't take orders anymore and began to imitate all of the crying boys. Then the nurse said, "You have to control yourself or leave!"

My Tourette's turned to one of the Vietnamese kids and said, "Du me may," which basically means, "Motherfucker."

"You're making fun of these babies," the nurse said. "You need to leave, sir!"

"No," I said. "I have Tourette's, fucker!"

"Leave, sir!" she insisted.

"No! I'm going to just stay here and take pictures of my kid."

Finally she gave up and left.

Having gotten used to being a father with Hassina, I was not worried about handling Husnah. Why be afraid of handling my own kid? When she reached three months old, I started changing her diapers. I also fed her and watched her when she crawled on the stairs.

As Husnah grew older, she liked to mimic my Tourette's – not to make fun of me, but just because she found it funny. She started imitating me when she was eight or nine months old. When she was about a year and a half, she started saying curse words. If she heard me saying, "Fuck you" or "Cusi!" (bitch) or "horny," she would repeat the words exactly. Soon she started to say curse words on her own. Sometimes she would whisper "horny, horny" or "Fuck you," but when Weda or I questioned her, she would say, "I said 'Barney' and 'I love you!'" A clever girl!

Once when we were riding in the car, and my brother Akbar was with us, Husnah started mimicking my curses words. Her older sister turned to Akbar and said, "Uncle, it's okay. Maybe my sister has Tourette's like my dad." Thankfully, Husnah doesn't have Tourette's, but she does like to imitate her dad! However, she doesn't imitate me in public.

Hassina is also protective of me in public. When she was about three, she would tell off other people who made fun of my Tourette's. "Don't make fun of my daddy," she would say. And if someone looked at me funny, she would come over and sit on my lap and kiss me and say, "I'm daddy's daughter." There would be a proud and defiant look in her eyes. And she would never repeat or make fun of the bad words my Tourette's would say. Sometimes, kids in Hassina's pre-school class would laugh when they heard me say, "Fuck you. Fuck you." But Hassina just ignored it. Truly, she made me stronger.

Because I grew up in a bad neighborhood in San Diego, where robberies were occurring all the time, I developed very sensitive hearing. Whenever I hear the slightest sounds at night, I wake up. If the girls are making any noises, I hear them. If there are noises outside, I hear those as well.

There's nothing is this world more important to me than my kids and wife. In our house, the kids come first. When Hassina turned four, Weda said, "I want to make my daughter a tennis player. I want my daughter to be the best athlete in the world!" Hassina is a very smart girl – and she gets her smarts from her mom! Weda and I both want the best for her and her younger sister.

Today, I love to play all kinds of games with my girls: hide and seek, Superman, football. Yes, they know how to hike the ball and run for a pass. When I say "hike," Hassina runs to receive the ball. But before I throw the ball, my Tourette's sometimes says, "Fuck you" – she then stops, comes back to me and says, "Let's start over." I can see that she wants me to learn how to manage my Tourette's and not swear during the game. I also have fun spraying my girls with the garden hose. Once my Tourette's shouted, "Fire, fire, I'm going to turn you off!" My girls looked at me, and Hassina said, "Whatever dad! Are you okay?"

Because I play so much with my daughters, they think of me as both their playmate and their father. Sometimes that means that they don't take me quite as seriously as they take their mother. When I tell Hassina to get ready for school, she may say she is tired. Then I say, "I'll tell your mom you don't want to go."

Immediately, she says, "I'm going!"

I love taking my kids shopping and showing them off to everyone. Lots of guys like me don't get that opportunity. I am thinking of changing my license plate to "I'm lucky."

My dad had bought a house in Tracy in 2003. He was one of the first to buy a house in this new development. People sometimes call Tracy a "cow town" because it was undeveloped for a long time and was populated mainly by cattle ranches. That same year, my sister also bought a house nearby. Although Weda's sister said she hated Tracy, I eventually convinced Weda to move there. "It's quiet, nice and safe," I said. In early 2005, we bought a house there. It was a model house that had been upgraded. It was supposed to come with the furniture, but the seller cheated us out of it!

Shortly after moving into the new house, Weda quit her job at the mortgage company. Her boss was a two-faced backstabber who cheated us out of thousands of dollars and was always ordering us around. He had promised to provide us with hospital insurance but didn't follow through, so we were left with big hospital bills from Weda's pregnancy with Husnah.

After Weda left the company, she focused on getting her own business license. In the meantime we worked under a friend's broker's license. We continued to work as a mort-gage team. In the last year and a half we progressed from working out of our garage to renting a small office to renting a huge one. We now have three offices. Our latest office is in an old opera house.

Weda continues to help me to be strong. She encourages me to stand up for myself, and she also intervenes on my behalf. Her view is "Screw everybody! If they don't like your Tourette's, they can leave." She has told more than a few taunters to "Go fuck off!" And I have done the same.

I remember eating in an expensive restaurant in Beverly Hills. I was twitching, and the waiter said to me, "You need to leave, sir."

"I have Tourette's," I said. He looked at me funny, so I got angry and said, "Fuck off, go get my food, asshole!"

Sometimes, when someone messes with me when Weda is at my side, I say, "I have Tourette's, and I have a beautiful life. Look who I take home every night! Who do you take home, asshole? Go fuck yourself!"

I have to admit that I feel stronger when I'm with my wife and kids. Then I feel I'm not handicapped. I can go anywhere around the world and be strong. I can tell people off.

Weda has always confronted people with attitudes. If a

salesperson is rude to her at a store, she'll say, "You need to change your attitude! I don't think you're going to succeed in life with an attitude like that!" She has told me that when people insult me, she thinks they are not worthy enough to deserve an explanation. When she hears someone say to me, "I don't care what he has," she just wants to sock the guy in the mouth. Once she told a guy, "You are no better than he is. You are mentally retarded: you can't feel what another person is feeling!"

Before I met my wife, I used to hide from stadiums and other public places. Now I go everywhere. But I do have some strategies for keeping my Tourette's under control. For example, when I'm in a restaurant, I may put Coke in my mouth to keep from making noises. But if I start laughing, I spit out the Coke! Sometimes, people are so stupid that they don't even notice!

Despite having some strategies for coping with public situations, I still find it hard to be in public. I generally don't eat in restaurants alone because I'm worried that I'll offend someone, who will pick a fight or call the police. When I'm at a restaurant with my family, it makes me sad to watch normal families sitting around the table and enjoying their meal without any strange interruptions and embarrassing outbursts. When I go on vacation with my family, I some-times get depressed because it's so crowded and hectic. Flying is also incredibly stressful, and I often get anxious for weeks before the flight. Even fun places can been stressful and depressing. In 2005, we took the kids to Disneyland. When I was standing in line with my girls, one parent said, "Let's leave and come back later when this idiot is not here because he's on drugs and it's scary to be around him." Hot weather aggravates also my syndrome, so I can't stay outside for very long on warm days and have to frequently change into cooler clothes. If I let myself get too hot, I start to feel as if I am choking. I look forward to summer rains that cool the air, and feel depressed when the rains are delayed.

There have been public occasions when strangers told my wife or kids that I'm handicapped and crazy and a troublemaker. Some people even told Weda that she could do better.

To avoid upsetting people with my Tourette's, I have avoided going to numerous weddings, parties, shows and public events. Generally, I don't take my kids to school or attend school meetings because I know my presence is not appreciated there. I even avoid their dance classes because so many of the kids' parents don't like me cursing and twitching.

People need to understand that I curse everybody. I don't mean it. It's my Tourette's that does it. I'm – it's – an equal opportunity curser!

I wouldn't be here without my wife. I'm blessed with a good woman! If Weda had caught me 10 years earlier, I'd be a different person: better, stronger, more confident. But everything I experienced in life was for a purpose. I've learned from the good and the bad. I know what's it's like to be on medicine and off medicine, to be lonely and to be loved. Sometimes I've cried to my wife that I wish I didn't have Tourette's, but I'm not ashamed anymore.

I also know what it's like to be on and off cigarettes. I started smoking when I was working at the Nissan dealership. I stopped and then started and then stopped and then started again. Smoking gives me diarrhea and spins my head. The only time I like to smoke is 1:00 or 2:00 in the afternoon or 9:00 or 10:00 or 11:00 at night. It relaxes me. It relaxes my body, makes me less stressed. I especially like smoking in cold weather. When I don't smoke, I get a migraine headache.

But recently I asked myself, "Why are you killing yourself?" I was smoking anywhere from four cigarettes to an entire pack each day. I told myself, "You had a pink lung.

Now you have a dark lung!" Sometimes I'd go behind Weda's back, but when I saw her, my Tourette's would say, "I smoked! I smoked!" It was always giving me away!

Weda's response is: "If you love your daughters, stop smoking!" I have now stopped for a few months. A guy told me that if you swear on something and don't follow through, you should pay five or ten dollars to someone, as a donation. I considered that approach but decided not to do it. My promise to my wife and kids is good enough.

Tea is my new cigarette. Black tea – yes, caffeinated tea calms me down. I drink six to eight cups per day before I go to sleep! Recently, I cut out coffee because it hurts my stomach so much. When my body feels strained, I like to listen to music or watch TV.

Some people have suggested that I take up meditation. I've tried it a couple of times, but it doesn't work for me. My Tourette's says, "Faking it. Get up, asshole. Fuck you, bullshiter." It calls my bluff! In one meditation class, my Tourette's started making faces and snoring sounds. The teacher said, "You have serious problems! Get out of here!" Tourette's won't let me change. I spit on one of the meditators, and to another I said, "Get off me, stop raping me!"

Tourette's controls me 99 percent of the time. It doesn't echo what I'm thinking. The son of a bitch wants to get me in trouble. Obviously, it still upsets my wife sometimes.

One day I shaved really hard and got a bruise under my goatee. My Tourette's said to Weda, "Look, I gotta hickey." Weda has a right to be pissed. I think my Tourette's wants my wife to beat the shit out of me!

Sometimes I go into the bathroom and look in the mirror and say, "Motherfucker, you give me trouble for no reason!"

It talks back to me: "I'm going to get you in trouble, punk!"

There have been times when I was in an elevator, and my

Tourette's started saying, "OOOOOOOO!" like I'm whacking off. The elevator door opens, and a woman is staring at me with a facial expression that says, "I know what you were doing!"

If I do something good, my Tourette's will say, "Show off!" It certainly keeps me humble!

Many times I've prayed for my Tourette's to go away. Sometimes I actually bless my Tourette's, saying, "I bless you for who you are. I thank you for who you are. I have to live with you."

The funny thing is that when I calm down, I miss him. I get bored. "Where are you, man?" I say. "Come on, bro, let's have some fun!"

"I'm here, asshole!" he would say. Tourette's and I are like two persons in one body. I'm really involved with him.

If I cured my Tourette's – and I've tried every kind of herb and approach – I'd be calmer and not as funny. I'd be a different person.

When I'm washing the car, I have conversations with my Tourette's. The neighbors think I'm talking to someone. One neighbor told me, "We didn't want to come outside because you were so pissed off at someone."

My Tourette's sleeps during the day sometimes. We wake each other up. We are a tag team in making people laugh and understand. I miss Tourette's when he's not around, and he misses me.

When I'm talking to people, Tourette's gives me ideas and advice. When I'm talking to my clients and forget something, he reminds me. When he gets caught saying things, I back him up. We're like a comedy team in one body. Tourette's made me who I am: funny. Without him, I wouldn't be funny enough. He tells me what to say. If he went away, people would hate me because I would be boring and sad. I'd be more like an older person or an old fart.

If my Tourette's left, Weda wouldn't miss him. She finds

him funny but knows how much suffering he causes me.

My wife is a very educated and classy woman. Lots of other wives I know aren't. My Tourette's says to them, "You dumb fuckers!" Sometimes I feel sorry for other people's wives who aren't educated. I just sit there and think, "Okay, Weda, show these bastards what you know!" I'm proud of her being so educated. She has also helped me to be very educated in life.

Tourette's is an amazing gift that attracts and inspires a lot of people. I encourage people to listen. They are amazed and shocked by what I have and ask a lot of questions. This is my time to educate people about what I have. It's my duty to let the world know. Sometimes I say to God, "Thank you for choosing me, God, because I can control it better than any other human being. At least I'm not crippled, I'm not blind, I'm not handicapped."

Technically, I deserve disability payments. In 1997, I even applied for disability. But when I went to the office, I saw a 400-pound woman sitting there and thought, "You need the money more than I do. I don't need it." So I decided not to pursue it. It would have also involved a bunch of hassles like seeing a doctor and attending a class. I had enough of doctors! And if I got a monthly check, I'd probably just sit home and get fat and ugly. Besides, the government would just be taking tax money from my wife and giving it to me!

I say to everyone, "Whatever you have, whoever you are, never give up!" I am proud of who I am and what I do and what I have.

God has given everything to me. A few years ago Weda and I were driving our 1980 Honda Accord, and we saw a Mercedes S500. Weda said, "Do you think we can have that car one day?"

"If God has given me to you, then we can have that and plenty more!" I replied.

The day came when she drove that car. Then we were

driving along and saw a Hummer H2. Weda said, "Do you think we can have that car one day?"

"Of course, we're going to have a Hummer," I replied. And sure enough we eventually bought one.

Then one day we were driving, and Weda pointed to a Mercedes SL500 and asked if we would have that one day, and I said, "We're going to have that too!" And we did.

God has been good to us! We are grateful for what we have and make sure to send a share to poor people. We believe that the more we give, the more God gives. But we don't give in order to get good will from God; we do it to help others. You have to have the heart to share with others.

Weda and I share our hearts. Some people see us as showing off. The reality is that people need help, and we have the heart to help them. God acts through people. My wife always says, "Thank God, not me. I'm the middle woman." We help our clients too. If they are short of their mortgage payments, we will often help them out for a few months. We don't want to watch people suffer. As Weda says, "We don't take anything with us. It is all rented. We only take our good deeds with us."

Chapter 8
Some of the Things
My Tourette's Said and
Did in Public

One day I went to shop at the grocery store by myself, and while I was shopping, I started to call out names like "I'm a fag, I'm a fag," and all of a sudden a young girl looked at me and said, "It's nice to know that someone at least admits who they really are." Of course, she didn't know I have Tourette's. When I tried to explain it to her, she just laughed hard and went away.

While I am driving my car, I often give the finger to people who stop next to me at a stoplight. Suddenly, I start flipping them off, and usually one or two people will see it and start cursing me. I just drive off as fast as I can, but sometimes they chase after me. Fortunately, no one has ever caught me.

When I am at a public bathroom, I often start making noises as if I were taking a leak or a shit. Then, I'll begin to scream words like "fuck me hard" or "suck me, baby" or "lick my nuts" or "I'm a fag" or "dude, suck my toes." As people come in and hear me, they freak out. When I walk out, everyone stares at me. And there have been times at movie theatres when the manager came in and said out loud, "Don't come here again, you sick bastard." When I try to explain, he just doesn't want to listen. One guy once said, "Like go and jack off somewhere else, asshole!" So I walked as fast as I could to my car and drove off.

One day I was at 7eleven, and there was a guy working at the cash register from India who wore a turban. Suddenly, I started calling him names like "you Gandhi fucker" and "you bulletproof turban, ice cream cone head." When he heard me saying these terrible words, he said, "Get out of my store!" I tried to explain, "Please understand that what I have, sir, is Tourette's syndrome." He replied, "Shut up. I am not a terrorist, you bastard!" I tried to explain that the syndrome is called "Tourette's" and that I was not calling him any name like "terrorist." Still, he kicked me out of the store and almost called the cops on me.

One day when I went to put gas in my car, I started screaming, "I will blow up the tank. I will burn the gas station. I will light it with matches." The gas station employee approached me and said, "What are you saying? You are scaring my clients. Leave or I'll call the cops." I said, "No, I have Tourette's syndrome, and I am sick and tired of everyone not understanding me, so when I am done, I will leave." He replied, "Fine, I will call the cops." I decided to run and drive off quickly before the cops arrived. The cops would probably not know what the syndrome is and would arrest me, thinking I was on drugs.

One day I was at the airport, flying to another city. As I boarded the plane, I started to say "I got a bomb." Everyone looked at me. I put my head down but said it again. A lady near me looked at me and said, "Excuse me, kid, did you say you have a bomb?" I replied, "No, I don't. I have Tourette's syndrome, and I can't control what I say." She seemed satisfied and said,"Okay." But then I said, "I got a gun and a bomb." I thought, now I'm going to get arrested. The flight attendant approached me and said, "Sir, do you have Tourette's syndrome?" I replied, "Yes, yes, I do. Do you know what it is?" She said, "Yes, I know." Wow, did I feel relieved. My ass was saved by that flight attendant. She told everyone what I have and said, "Don't worry. It's a syndrome that makes people say lots of words. Just ignore him." What an experience that was!

Once I went with my parents to see a house for sale. I told the house owner, "I will kill you. I will kill you." He was frightened and asked my dad, "Is your son serious about what he's saying?" Dad said, "Don't worry. He has this syndrome which he can't help what he says." The guy said, "Okay." Then suddenly my Tourette's said, "I will rape your daughter. I will fuck her. I will kill her. I will doggy style her." That was too much for the guy. He cursed me and my dad and said, "Get the fuck out of the house or else I'll call the police." Then he screamed real loud, "I will kill you, you asshole, if you touch my daughter, and I will take down your license plate number in case of any problem to my family." Dad tried to explain what I had: "It's a syndrome called Tourette's syndrome." But the guy started to throw things at the car, so we quickly left. Dad was very upset at the syndrome and at the home owner.

One time I went to the restaurant and started to order the food. When I got my food, there were so many people at the restaurant that as soon as I started to eat my first bite, I started to yell out, "Yuk, there's a cockroach in my food. This food has hair in it. This food has shit in it. This food has poison. Lick the hair nuts of the food, assholes! It's got pussy hairs and dick hairs." Suddenly, the manager stormed up to me and said, "Sir, we need you to leave please because you are too drunk or on drugs. Or we'll call the police on you." I started to explain what I have, but the manager said, "Whatever! Leave now or we'll call the police because you are scaring all the customers."

Once I went for a job interview at a car dealership and was waiting for the manager to interview me. Suddenly, I got called into his office. He was a black skinned person. I said, "Oh, God, help me please!" Then Tourette's said, "Nigger, nigger." And the manager said, "What did you say?" Before I could explain, he just told me off and kicked me out. There went my interview!

Once I went with my wife to see Planet of the Apes. A few minutes into the movie, the apes began making gorillas noises. Well, my Tourette's started making the same sounds, and everyone got mad. Some guy sitting near us screamed out, "Whoever is making those noises better stop or I'll call security." I kept making the noises because I couldn't stop the syndrome. Another group of guys sitting toward the front shouted to the complainer, "Stop making noise, asshole." The complainer replied, "Fuck you, it's not us." Then the two groups of guys got into a fight. I just snuck out of the theatre as the fight was breaking out.

One day I went to visit my mom at the hospital when she was very sick. She was sharing a room with another woman. I said to the woman, "I will kill you. I will pull out your I.V. I will choke you." The lady screamed, "Help me! Help me!" Suddenly, the nurses ran in and said, "What is wrong, madam?" She replied, "He said he would kill me. Help me, please! This kid is dangerous!" I explained to the nurses what I had, and they understood, but the woman did not. She asked the nurses to kick me out of the room, and they did. My mom watched this entire episode with a smile on her face. She was used to this shit!

One time I was hospitalized to have surgery on my appendix. After the surgery, I asked the nurses taking care of me, "Do you want to fuck me?" They were really mad, but I said to one of them, "Please suck my camel dick and lick my nuts and blow me, you chinless bitch. I will rape you tonight." Many nurses don't know what the syndrome is. They went to tell the security guard to watch out for me. After I was released, one nurse said to me, "Get some help, please!"

One day I got pulled over by the police for speeding. I started twitching, and he said, "Are you okay." I said, "Yeah, and I'm on drugs. And I'm a fag. I got a gun…" He interrupted me and said, "Are you really on drugs? Do you really have gun?" I replied, "I have Tourette's syndrome." He said, "Yeah, sure, so does my mom! Where is your doctor's letter or any type of proof of what syndrome you have." All I could do was tell him what I have and try to make him understand. He did some tests on me, like the DUI test, and when I passed, he wrote me a ticket. Then he said, "Next time get some type of a letter to carry with you so if you ever get pulled over by any other police officers, they won't shoot you or arrest you for what you say."

One day I went to Blockbuster to rent a movie. As I was walking around the store, I suddenly said in a loud voice, "I am stealing movies in my jacket!" After I repeated this several times, one of the store clerks walked up to me and said, "What part of your jacket are the movies in?" I started to tell the clerk that I have Tourette's syndrome and that I just say things that I don't mean, but he said, "Let me search you or I will call the cops." Since I don't like to see cops, I let them search me. But during the search, I kept saying, "Don't touch my dick. Don't touch my ass. Slap me in the ass!" He immediately stopped searching me and said, "Just get the fuck out of the store, you sick bastard!"

Once I went to the emergency hospital at night, and as I was waiting in the waiting room for my turn, I saw this really fat woman come in. She sat right next to me. What a mistake she made! My syndrome started to say, "Fat ass! Fat ass! Fat ass! Fat fuck, start dieting, fat ass." She looked at me like a mean bulldog and said, "I'll kick your skinny ass, asshole!" I started to explain to her what I have, but she just hit me with her purse. The hospital security came over and grabbed her. She yelled, "So what if I am fat! I am trying to lose weight, asshole!" She opened up in front of everyone and told them what she was going through.

One time I was invited to a family wedding party. When I arrived, I told my family and the people sitting next to me, "I fucked the bride already!" They looked at me in shock, and I said, "She sucked my dick." These people were members of the bride's family. They turned to my parents and said, "Please watch your son's mouth!" My dad explained what I have, and they understood. When the wedding started and everyone began dancing, I also got up to dance. I was twitching while I was dancing and kept bumping into other people. Suddenly, everyone started to push around everyone else and I got pushed around too. The singer said, "Please, people, relax!" So everyone stopped dancing and pointed at me, indicating that I had started the pushing. The singer said to me, "Please don't drink too much alcohol!" I wasn't even drinking! After the music stopped, it was time for everyone to eat dinner. Once again my syndrome kicked in. I began repeating aloud, "I'm a fag" and "I fucked the bride in the ass." Everyone looked at me, and I said, "I raped the bitch." Suddenly, everyone started to laugh, and the family came up to me and said they wanted me to leave as soon as possible or otherwise I would get my ass kicked. After all the things I said, I was lucky to walk out of the wedding alive!

Once I was at my wife's office doing some telemarketing to get her clients for refinancing mortgages. During one of the calls to a client's house, I said, "Fuck you!" The client said, "Excuse me, what did you say?" I said, "I'm sorry, but is there anyone else on your phone, sir?" I am quick in saving my ass: I made the client think there was someone taping our phone call and periodically cursing at us. Throughout the whole conversation, the client thought it was someone else that was cursing at us, so he talked to me, and I made the deal.

One time I appeared in court as a witness to a crime. After I was sworn in, I was asked if I had seen the defendant stab the victim. I said, "Yes, there he is." And then I said, "I lied." The judge looked at me, and my attorney got up and explained to the judge what I have. But then my Tourette's picked on the judge and started calling her names like, "Fat ass, look at me" and "Fat Shamu, look at me." You could see that the lawyers were holding in their laughter. But throughout the trial, my syndrome was cursing at the judge, and the lawyers and everyone else at the court house could barely hold in their laughter.

Sometimes, when I'm somewhere alone, I look around to be sure no one is around me, and then I start twitching and cursing and saying things like, "I'm fag. I'll jack off. I got fucked." My syndrome may even scream sounds that imitate

113

two people having sex. When people appear, they look at me and laugh, probably thinking I'm on drugs or am crazy.

I used to be the used car buyer at a car dealership. I remember one of the first times I was sent to the auctions to buy cars for the dealership. I started twitching, but the auctioneers weren't aware of what I have. They were just selling me cars left and right as my hands were twitching up and down. Whenever they looked at me, I kept twitching my eyes and head. They kept selling me the cars even though I was not even betting! In fact, they thought that my raising my hands and moving my head meant that they had sold me over 22 cars in one day! I argued with them that I hadn't purchased the cars, but they said, "Sorry, you've bet on the auction day, and you're responsible for all the buying for this dealership." I explained to them that I have Tourette's, but they insisted "Too bad. You own these vehicles and won't be allowed any more unless you take responsibility for what you have." I thought it was really funny, and fortunately so did my boss and the other employees at the dealership.

My neighbors once asked me to watch their house. They gave me their key because they were going away for Christmas. When they returned from their trip, my Tourette's said to them, "I jacked off on your beds!" They looked at me weirdly, and my Tourette's said, "I stole your CD's. And I killed someone in your house." The neighbors knew a little about what I have, but one day they came over to my house and asked me, "Did you really jack off in our house? And, by the way, we really think we are missing some CD's." I said, "No, I didn't do those things. I have Tourette's syndrome." After a few weeks they told everyone what I said and that they were scared of me. I found it all very funny.

Sometimes, when I see someone's wife or husband, I start to make faces at them. I may even say, "I farted" or "I stink" or "You stink" or "I will kiss you" or "I will kick you in the ass." Or when they are telling a story to me and my wife, I start saying, "You liars." They look at me and say, "We're not lying." I say, "I'm sorry. It's my syndrome, so excuse me for what I say." The minute they start to talk, I say, "Yeah, yeah, shut up!" It's so funny that they start laughing.

When I go to the Oakland Raiders games, I usually sit with the Raiders fans because I am a fan too. But sometimes I yell, "Fuck the Raiders. They suck." When the fans look at me, I turn my face the other way and say, "Who the hell is saying that?" They think it's someone else! Once I saw some black people sitting in front of me, and I said, "Nig, nig, nig." They turned around and looked at me and said, "Who is saying that?" Suddenly, I said some other words like, "Fat ass nigger." Just at that moment, a fight broke out among some Mexicans sitting behind me, so the black people got up and pushed me out of the way and began beating the Mexicans. The Mexicans had nothing to do with what was said, but they got their asses beaten anyway. My syndrome and I were lucky to get away without a beating!

One day I was eating at a Mexican restaurant. I kept saying bad words in Spanish like "panocha," which means "pussy." After every bite I took, I would say, "Good panocha, yes, juicy panocha." There were many people at the restaurant, and they got mad because they had their daughters and wives with them. One amigo got up and said, "You like pussy?" I said, "What are you saying?" He said, "You like pussy, so go and get it somewhere else because this is a restaurant not a panocha restaurant. Go before I kill you!" I said, "I have a sickness." He said, "Yeah, my friend, you have sickness of not getting panocha, so go get it and you'll be no more sick."

I had to leave because this guy was stupid and wouldn't understand me.

I was at a Subway restaurant one day getting some sandwiches. The cashiers and people making the sandwiches were from India. When it was my turn to order, the cashier said, "What kind of sandwich do you want?" My syndrome said, "Gandhi sandwich. Turban sandwich." The guy said, "Are you making fun of my race?" I said, "No, fuck you." He didn't know what I have, so he refused to serve me. He said, "Get out of my store you stupid Mexican." He didn't realize I am from Afghanistan. Because I resemble Hispanic people, he called me names in Spanish!

Once I went to visit Mexico with some friends. On our way back to America, we came to the border, where they check your green cards and American citizenship paperwork. The guards ask, "How was your stay? What have you brought to take back to your homeland?" My syndrome suddenly said, "Drugs, drugs, drugs." The guards told me to pull over to the right side of the road. They searched the car and me and my brothers and friends. Of course, they didn't find anything. Then they asked my brothers and friends, "Is your friend the one who said there are drugs in the car?" One of my friends explained that I have Tourette's and that it is a sickness of saying things. After the guards heard the story, they asked me separately what I have. I told them I have Tourette's. While I was explaining the syndrome, I suddenly said, "I have fake green cards. I am a fake person." The guards looked alarmed and made us wait for hours. Finally, they came and released us from all charges. They told my brothers and friends, "Don't bring him here again. If we're not here and the guards don't understand his syndrome, they'll put him in jail for months until they find out what's wrong with him." When we got back home, we told my family what happened, and they all laughed.

One day I went out with some friends to a club. I said aloud, "I'm gay. I'm gay." Some guys approached me and said, "Are you really a fag?" I said, "No I'm not, assholes." They said, "What?" And I said, "Fuck you guys, suck my dick, fuck your sisters, you mother fuckers." Then I began to twitch and said, "I have AIDS, AIDS, AIDS." These guys started to get scared and just ran as far as they could from me because they freaked out.

I went to the mall one day. As I was shopping, I made some weird noises, and an old lady with her young daughter approached me. She said, "Do you have a bird or a parakeet with you making those cute bird songs? My husband used to listen to bird songs. Could you tell me where I can buy one of the singing birds you have inside your jacket." I said, "Madam, I don't have a bird in my jacket. It's me making those noises. I have Tourette's syndrome." She said, "Is that what the birds have when they sing?" I just started laughing and walked away.

One day I was at the airport waiting in line with my wife. I was wearing a beautiful suit and suddenly began twitching and talking to myself over my shoulder. A woman in line said, "Excuse me, sir, are you an FBI agent?" I said, "No, madam, I have Tourette's syndrome. She said, "I don't believe what you're saying you have. It's known that you have to keep secret who you are, and we are glad to have secret agents in the airport flying with us. We feel much safer." Once we got on the plane, she told the passengers that I'm an FBI agent so they don't have to worry – they are safe!

Once I went to the car rental store. The guy behind the counter said, "I.D. and credit card, please." When I opened my wallet, I said, "Fake license. Fake credit card." The guy looked hard at me and asked for a second I.D. I didn't have one. The guy began questioning me and said, "We think this is not your I.D. and credit card, so we won't rent a car to you until you show us a second I.D." Soon the cops showed up. They checked the I.D. and credit card and confirmed that they belonged to me. As the cops were leaving, they asked, "Why did you say this is a fake I.D. and credit card?" I said, "I tried to explain to the car rental people what I have but you (police) came at me so quickly that I never thought of explaining what I have." The police laughed and left, and the car rental people laughed too.

Once I was at the gym working out. I was running on the jogging machine next to several other people who were running on the machines. Suddenly I began twitching. The twitching got so strong that I flew back and hit the other runners on the nearby machines. Everyone started to laugh. Though I was hurt, I found it funny too.

I was riding my bicycle on a busy street one day. I was twitching a little bit, but suddenly I began twitching more and more and ran right into a police motorcycle who was parked on the side of the road to radar cars for speeding. After I ran into him, he just laughed at me. Instead of finding out what happened to me, he just laughed and asked me if I was okay. He said, "Walk home instead riding when you're twitching. And be careful." He was still laughing as I was leaving.

One day I was at the court house trying to find out what happened to my ticket. The line was so long. I just waited and prayed I wouldn't say anything that would upset people. Suddenly, my syndrome said, "Fat ass. Nigger. Nigger." Two couples near me began laughing so hard at what I was saying that my Tourette's suddenly started calling them names too: "Fuck off, stupid Mexicans. Suck my camel dick." My twitching got so bad that they got scared and went to tell the security guard how I was mistreating them and was on some kind of drugs. After I took care of my ticket, I went out the door but was pulled over by a police motorcycle just outside the court house. The cop asked me, "What drug are you on?" I laughed, then he said, "What's so funny?" I said, "I have Tourette's syndrome that causes me to twitch and curse so those two who complained were not aware of what I have, so they came and told you guys I'm on drugs." After the cop understood what happened, he laughed too and said, "Be careful wherever you go!"

Once I was standing in line behind a girl at a take out restaurant, my Tourette's said, "Doggy style. Doggy style." The girl turned around and slapped me. I said, "I've got Tourette's." She said, "You really have Tourette's?" I said, "Yes." She said, "I'm sorry. Can I have your autograph? Oh, you're so lucky! You're so cute!" I said, "You're crazy, girl! You slap me and then you want my autograph! If this were Afghanistan, I would have knocked your ass out!"

One time I was at the flea market. As I was buying some fabric from these two Chinese guys, I suddenly started to scream and make noises. One guy asked me, "Why do you keep saying 'Chinese fuckers,' 'Chinese bitches'? Why are you so upset at Chinese people?" The other guy then said to me, "Is there a song you are singing or do you have a WalkMan on because I hear these Chinese noises in the karate movies." I laughed and said, "No, I have Tourette's syndrome." He said, "You have a bad disease." I said, "No, not at all." He said, "It's fuckin crazy shit, my friend." I said, "It's God's gift." He said, "God hates you because you are not a good person because you keep saying 'Fuck Chinese people.'" I tried to explain, but they were so mad that they would have chopped me into sushi meat. I quickly took off. They threw pencils at me and cursed me in English: "Go fuck yourself, you stupid Mexican asshole." They thought I was Mexican!

Once I went to get some coffee, and as I was standing in line, I said, "I got laid, bitch." Several people looked at me funny, and I said, "I got laid. I got a blow job. I got fucked five times today." A young girl approached me and said, "That's nice. At least someone got laid today!" I said, "No, no, I have a syndrome." She said, "What? Do you have a sex syndrome?" I said, "No, no, I have Tourette's." She said, "How do you get that? Can I get that too? Is there any pill for that?" "No, it's called Tourette's syndrome." "I'd like to have that so I can feel the same way!"

I didn't ask for all of these things, good and bad, to happen to me. But I do know one thing: that I am a human being with a soul. I want to enjoy life to the max. I want to go out with my wife and my family. I want to attend my children's school functions. I want to play at the park with my daughters without anyone interfering. In short, I just want to live my life normally!

I simply want people to ask themselves how they would feel if they were like me? Or how would they feel if their children or grandchildren were like me? Would you mistreat your loved ones the way so many people have mistreated me? I am asking, I am imploring, everyone who reads this book to please change your point of view about individuals with disabilities. Please respect everyone equally. After all, we are all human, and no human being is perfect. But from another perspective, all of us are perfect. "Perfect" means "complete, whole."

Wow! So many people think that I'm on drugs, that I'm

sick, that I'm crazy, that I'm nuts. Before reading this book, you too might have thought I was nuts. What do you think now?

I would like to dedicate this book to everyone out there who is perfect or imperfect. I think I am perfect. What do you think? Please send me an email to let me know what you think of me. My email address is wedashah@yahoo.com.

Thank you for reading my book! I hope you have learned a lot about Tourette's syndrome.